Ramon dos Reis Fontes
Christian Rodolfo Esteve Rothenberg

Wireless Network Emulation

with Mininet-WiFi

1st edition

Campinas
Christian Rodolfo Esteve Rothenberg
2019

Credits

Authors
Ramon dos Reis Fontes
Christian Rodolfo Esteve Rothenberg

Reviewers
Michel Daoud Yacoub

About the authors

Ramon dos Reis Fontes received the degree in Information Systems from the Faculty of Technology and Sciences (FTC), in 2009, the Master degree in Systems and Computing from Salvador University (UNIFACS), in 2013, and the Ph.D. degree in Electrical Engineering in the area of Computer Engineering from the University of Campinas (UNICAMP), in 2018. His research interests includes Software-Defined Networking (SDN), wireless networks, distributed systems, cloud and fog computing, Network Functions Virtualization (NFV), and security. Ramon has published several papers on conferences and journals, and has continuously contributed to the development of free and open source software through his Github account (`https://github.com/ramonfontes`). A variety of codes and instructions on how to reproduce his research works can be found at `https://github.com/ramonfontes/reproducible-research/`.

I would like to thank the readers for their interest in this book. Please do not hesitate to contact us if you need any help on any subject covered in this book. I would like to thank my friends, colleagues and teachers who have helped me in many ways. I would also like to thank Prof. Dr. Christian Rothenberg, counselor, advisor and co-author of this book, for sharing his wisdom and encouragement throughout my career at the Faculty of Electrical Engineering and Computing at UNICAMP.

My special thanks go to my beloved wife, Suian. This book would not be a reality without your continued support. I would also like to thank my parents, Helio and Conceição, for their incentives and support.

To my daughter, Pietra, I dedicate this book.

Christian Rodolfo Esteve Rothenberg is Professor at the Department of Computer Engineering and Industrial Automation (DCA) of the Faculty of Electrical Engineering and Computation (FEEC) at the University of Campinas (UNICAMP) since 2013. He holds the Telecommunication Engineering degree from the Technical University of Madrid (ETSIT - UPM), Spain, the M.Sc. (Dipl. Ing.) degree in Electrical Engineering and Information Technology from Darmstadt University of Technology (TUD), Germany, 2006, and the Ph.D. in Electrical Engineering from UNICAMP (2010). From 2010 to 2013, he worked as a senior researcher at CPqD R&D center in telecommunication on P&D projects in the area of IP platforms. He is the Principal Investigator of the Information & Networking Technologies Research & Innovation Group (INTRIG – `https://intrig.dca.fee.unicamp.br/`), CNPq Research Productivity Fellow level 2 (2017-2020), and CNPq Technological Development and Innovative Extension Fellow level 2 (2014-2016). His research interests include computer network architectures, virtualization, cloud computing, SDN, NFV, among others. He has 2 international patents and more than 120 magazine and conference publications, accumulating more than 6000 citations (h-index: 28, i10-index: 50+ – `https://scholar.google.com.br/citations?user=8PxuHPkAAAAJ&hl=en`).

The completion of a book is a great opportunity to reflect and express gratitude. Starting with our ancestors, in my case, my parents José Luis and Ana. In my academic life, I I thank all the teachers who influenced me with a special highlight to Professor Mauricio, PhD advisor, academic father, and friend, a key figure since I landed on this beloved Brazil. I am grateful for all the opportunities I have received from this country, its people, and institutions, including CPqD, FEEC, UNICAMP, the national funding agencies CNPq and FAPESP, Ericsson, among others. I thank students, from undergraduate to postgraduate, professional colleagues, and friends of everyday life. To our INTRIG group, and of course, to Prof. Dr. Ramon Fontes, the first PhD made in INTRIG, an example of graduate student and human being, father and co-author of this book that I am sure will contribute to the formation of more professionals. Finally, the most important vector in life, the family, my wife Marcela, my children Gabriel and Marina, my sources of energy and happiness. Thank you!

About the Reviewers

Daniel Senna

We would like to thank Daniel Senna, an editor at Textual Assessoria, for providing proofreading assistance.

Acknowledgements

The success of this project and the writing of this book were only possible thanks to the support, collaboration and trust of many people and institutions that helped to make them come true. Therefore, we would like to record our thanks.

We thank Katia Obraczka, professor at the University of California, Santa Cruz, California, for his valuable input and suggestions on Mininet-WiFi development steps. We also thank the *Institut National de Recherche en Informatique et en Automatique* (INRIA), especially to Thierry Turletti and Walid Dabbous, for receiving us at INRIA for six (6) months and for contributing in various aspects related to the development of Mininet-WiFi. For the financial support, we thank the *Fundação de Amparo à Pesquisa do Estado de São Paulo* (FAPESP), process 2014/18482-4 and *Conselho Nacional de Pesquisas* (CNPq), process 310930/2016-2. The INTRIG research group thanks Ericsson for the research funding received, without which the group would not have achieved its results, many of them leveraged by and contributing to Mininet-WiFi.

Thanks also to users, researchers, and/or developers who contributed to making this book a reality, more specifically: Prof. Dr. Chih-Heng Ke, from the National Quemoy University/Taiwan, for tips and shared experience on how wireless networks work; Brian Linkletter, for writing a tutorial, and helping spread Mininet-WiFi; Patrick Große, for developing a *Wmediumd* extension for Mininet-WiFi; and, of course, to the Mininet-WiFi community for all discussions that result in the development of an increasingly stable and complete emulator in terms of features supported.

Wireless Network Emulation with Mininet-WiFi
ISBN: 978-65-900571-5-0 (E-book)

Terms & Conditions

Table of Contents

I   Introduction

FAQ

References

Preface

We are witnessing an impressive revolution in the field of Computer Networks. Advances in wireless communications such as the imminent deployment of 5G networks worldwide, the ability to virtualize network infrastructures (e.g. Network Slicing and Network Function Virtualization) and to program their behavior (e.g. Software-Defined Networking) are concrete examples of this new era.

These advances enable the design, development and deployment of innovative mechanisms aimed at, for instance, higher resilience, performance, energy efficiency, and security of the network and service ecosystem. A key element to explore these new opportunities is the use of tools that enable prototyping and testing novel ideas at an early stage, without the constraints and complexities associated with employing a real infrastructure. This is precisely the role occupied by Mininet-WiFi, an environment that allows one to create, explore and experiment with software-defined wireless networks from a personal computer.

As an instructor of the Undergraduate and Graduate Networking courses at INF-UFRGS, I often assign students to develop new mechanisms on software-defined network infrastructures. It was a pleasant surprise when, in 2016, I began using Mininet-WiFi. This environment has dramatically expanded the scope of possible work we could do, enabling us to design a whole new set of proposals, such as routing algorithms for efficient mobile video streaming, handoff strategies with traffic fluctuation awareness and load balancing mechanisms. This type of work was challenging, if not impossible, to carry out in the classic Mininet environment, as it was beyond its scope to provide primitives for dealing specifically with wireless communication.

This book closes a cycle of development, innovation and transfer of new knowledge to society. By very didactically documenting and explaining how to use Mininet-WiFi through scripts, example codes, illustrations and other resources, the book will foster many new experiences like the ones just mentioned. There is no doubt that it will endure as an important work in the academic, industry and government sectors. I congratulate the authors for their praiseworthy initiative of advancing knowledge in this fascinating and fundamental field. There is no time to waste: the time has come to "roll up our sleeves" and begin our immersion in Mininet-WiFi. Good reading and enjoy!

Prof. Luciano Paschoal Gaspary
Institute of Informatics - UFRGS

Chapter Organization

This book is organized as follows:

Chapter I introduces theoretical fundamentals of wireless networks, software-defined wireless networks and also Mininet-WiFi. This chapter goes in-depth into concepts relevant to the learning objectives of this book. For a deeper understanding of the different topics explored, the reader will be provided references to relevant literature in the field;

Chapter II introduces the beginner level of Mininet-WiFi proficiency and is devoted solely to providing the working details of Mininet-WiFi, where its key functional aspects are described. If you are already proficient with Mininet-WiFi, you can focus on chapters III and IV instead. You do not need to be familiar with Mininet to use Mininet-WiFi, but if you are, you will certainly have a smoother feel as to how Mininet-WiFi works. The tutorials included in this chapter can be used as complementary activities in theory classes at the undergraduate level (e.g. EA074 at FEEC/UNICAMP), as well as in practical laboratory courses (e.g. EA080 at FEEC/UNICAMP);

Chapter III introduces the intermediate level of Mininet-WiFi proficiency, covers tutorials that employ wireless networking, software-defined wireless networking, as well as a number of concepts related to computer networking. This chapter also describes the use of some network applications, such as *tcpdump* and *Wireshark*. In addition to meeting the pedagogical goals of more advanced computer network classes such as those involving laboratory activities, the tutorials in this chapter are also suitable for graduate classes (e.g. IA369, IA376 at FEEC/UNICAMP) and specialization courses (e.g. INF-556 at IC/UNICAMP), as they allow experimental research to be carried in more complex scenarios, such as the development of SDN solutions using the OpenFlow protocol;

Finally, **Chapter IV** introduces the expert level of Mininet-WiFi proficiency, has tutorials about kernel manipulation, containers, security, IoT, vehicular networks, etc., with valuable information on adapting the OpenFlow protocol to wireless networks. This chapter is labeled as advanced because it requires more in-depth knowledge and the use of third-party applications. Therefore, the tutorials in this chapter are best suited for specialization and graduate courses, not only in classes but also as technical training for master's and doctoral students, thus helping the development of experimental research aimed at advancing the state of the art. However, nothing prevents curious readers from reproducing these tutorials, since they have similar walkthroughs, as well as the support provided by the codes from the previous chapters.

Conventions used in this book

To facilitate the reading of this book, the following conventions have been adopted:

italic: indicates foreign language words or program/tool names.

<*file*>: indicates files or scripts.

The symbols below represent:

 Complementary information to previously exposed content.

 Relevant alert or remark.

 Question regarding the topic being explored.

 Citations and other complementary sources.

 Demonstration videos.

 Requirement(s) For each existing experiment there will be an indication of the prerequisites to conduce it. For convenience, we have assigned the "script(s) only" label to the prerequisites requiring only the use of scripts that are already available for use. Since all scripts were coded with Mininet-WiFi in mind, we do not include Mininet-WiFi in the Prerequisites tab. The same goes for all packages that are installed during the Mininet-WiFi installation process, such as OVS, the OpenFlow protocol, etc.

Other conventions

As there is a tendency to replace tools from the *net-tools* package by those of the *iproute2* package in Linux operating systems, network tools like *iw* and *ip* are preferred for the tutorials. Nonetheless, programs from the *net-tools* package can also be used.

Finally, due to code update issues all scripts are available in a repository on Github (`https://github.com/ramonfontes/mn-wifi-book-en`).

Precautions

It is recommended that all tutorials available in this book be completed using the latest version of Mininet-WiFi available on Github. Should you, the reader, find any inconsistencies in the tutorials, you may contact the authors of this book at any time for clarification.

Although this book brings hands-on experience at all times, we recommend that you review each command or configuration beforehand so that the entire process can be understood.
Do not try to complete the tutorials without clearly understanding what is being done!

I must use Linux. But why?

Because the code base of Mininet-WiFi, Mininet, was developed for Linux systems. The development of Mininet-WiFi has maintained the same operating structure as that of Mininet. The Ubuntu operating system should be preferred, especially its Long Term Support (LTS) versions, as they are the most stable Ubuntu distributions.

Why open source code?

We will answer this question with a simple answer: because most of the time we (you, I and everyone) have the freedom to use the tool/program we want. Whether it is because we need to do work or academic research, or because we want to know more about Mininet-WiFi, or even because we need to modify it to suit our needs, we can choose. However, this seems like a ready answer, which we often receive as an answer by others when we wonder about the advantages of opening the source code of a particular program.

Arguing chronologically, we could say that without Mininet-WiFi, I, Ramon, would not have obtained a doctoral degree; many researchers would not have done their research; Mininet, the emulator Mininet-WiFi was based on, would probably not exist either, and so on. What we mean is that without open source philosophy, we would not have access to Mininet and would not have developed Mininet-WiFi. Just as Mininet would not have been developed without the previous development of its backbone and its subsequent availability for anyone to use. Most likely you would not even be reading this book now and many fewer persons would be interested in the subjects we covered in it.

Can you imagine how much research on other topics would be undermined by only focusing on the field of research covered in this book and ignoring other possibilities? Perhaps you will have a better idea as you complete the tutorials proposed throughout this book.

There is a whole chain that would be seriously impacted if the codes were not free to use. The main paper [14] about Mininet alone has had about 1500 direct citations, not to mention countless indirect citations by blogs and even the media.

Experiences: Impact, Reproducibility and Quality

If you are wondering whether it is worth researching and exposing your code to the public, even though it is still in the early stages of development, here are some reports of experiences we have gained throughout Mininet-WiFi development.

Impact. Making code, data, documentation and demonstration videos public has certainly contributed and still greatly contributes to increasing Mininet-WiFi's visibility. Although there has been no systematic and qualitative assessment of the Mininet-WiFi community, users have contributed to the project several times, whether by discussing or even suggesting code improvements and new implementations.

Reproducibility. Making data public and reproducible is not always a simple task. By the way, writing a book whose tutorials users can complete without any setbacks is not easy. Most likely there will be one or another tutorial that will not flow as expected. This is due to several factors, such as differences in tool versions, issues that may be related to the operating system, hardware, etc. Throughout the development of Mininet-WiFi, we had a hard time reproducing experiments by other researchers, as there was often not enough information to do so. For this reason, we have chosen not only to make our experiments public, but also to describe how they can be reproduced. Making research reproducible generally adds credibility to its respective work and obtained results.

Quality. In a broader sense of research quality, all the experiences gained throughout the development of Mininet-WiFi allowed us to learn and refine our research. Although ensuring the reproducibility of a project increases workload, reproducible work has a number of significant advantages, such as: (i) synergy with open source functionality, as the latter increases the chances of direct and indirect reproducibility and, consequently, (ii) greater impact, since the chances of researchers using the solutions proposed by reproducible works increase; (iii) improvement of programming habits, wherein special attention is given to code quality; (iv) encouragement of the use of scientific workflows, as researchers are carefully concerned with providing reliable results so that anyone can produce results similar to those they have obtained.

So if you have the opportunity, and if your code is not a license, patent, or any other copyrighted content, try making your code public!

List of Figures

List of Tables

List of Acronyms

IoT	Internet of Things
LTE	Long-Term Evolution
LWAPP	Lightweight Access Point Protocol
MCS	Modulation and Coding Scheme
MIMO	Multiple Input, Multiple Output
MLME	Media Access Control Sublayer Management Entity
MPTCP	MultiPath TCP
MQTT	Message Queuing Telemetry Transport
NFV	Network Function Virtualization
OF	OpenFlow
ONF	Open Networking Foundation
OVSAP	OpenvSwitch Access Point
RSSI	Received Signal Strength Indicator
RTC	Request To Receive
RTS	Request To Send
SDN	Software Defined Networking
SDWN	Software Defined Wireless Networking
SNR	Signal to Noise Ratio
SSID	Service Set Identifier
STA	Station
SUMO	Simulation of Urban MObility
TC	Traffic Control
UserAP	User level Access Point
VANET	Vehicular Ad hoc NETwork
WLAN	Wireless Local Area Network

Introduction

1   Background **3**

1. Background

1.1 Wireless communications

Wireless communications continues to be one of the most vibrant fields in the telecommunications sector. Although they began in the late nineteenth and early twentieth centuries, wireless communication research and development activities intensified between the 1970s to 1990s, fueled by a growing demand for increasingly better connectivity. Initially driven by the development of cell phones for voice services and then data applications, wireless technologies keep evolving, fostered by new forms of content creation and consumption and interaction between humans, machines and everyday objects, a trend commonly known as the Internet of Things (IoT).

Conventional wireless communication networks encompass several elements, the most basic of which are listed below: (i) the wireless terminals - such as laptops, smartphones, which are the interface between the user and the network; (ii) radio links, which connect the terminals to an agent providing the network coverage service; (iii) base stations, which function as the coverage agents; (iv) switching and control centers, which concentrate the base stations and connect them to other communication services.

There are numerous technologies that provide wireless services, such as Bluetooth, LTE, Zigbee, WiFi, among other means. Wireless communications have unique features that make them distinct from other technologies. One of them, and certainly the most important one, is the propagation of radio waves. A signal propagating from one point to another undergoes three types of phenomena, namely: attenuation, long-term fading and short-term fading. Attenuation refers to loss of transmission when the receiver moves away from the source. Long-term fading refers to conditions when the average signal changes slowly over time due to obstructions to the signal path, such as buildings, trees, etc. Short-term fading refers to quick fluctuations of the signal due to reflection, scattering and diffraction. There is also the problem of interference by services using the same frequency or even approximate frequencies.

Due to the increasing worldwide demand for wireless communications, new technologies are emerging so that systems can meet this demand. In any case, the development of any system, and, more specifically, wireless systems, requires a deep knowledge of the phenomena involved. Figure 1.1 exem-

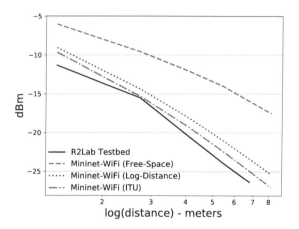

Figure 1.1: RSSI. Source: [18]

plifies the phenomenon of path loss by showing how the Received Signal Strength Indicator (RSSI), in dBm, oscillates in relation to the physical distance between a base station and a wireless station. The figure compares the estimations of different propagation models described in the literature (*Free-Space, Log-Distance, ITU*) - which are available in the Mininet-WiFi emulator - compared to measurements taken in a laboratory environment, the R2Lab[1] testbed. Figure 1.2, in turn, illustrates the phenomena of long-term and short-term fading.

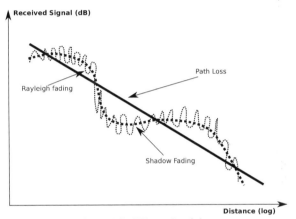

Figure 1.2: Effect of path loss.

- M. D. Yacoub, *Foundations Of Mobile Radio Engineering*. CRC Press, 1993. ISBN: 978-0849386770
- T. Rappaport, *Wireless Communications: Principles and Practice*, Pearson Education India, 2010. ISBN: 978-0130422323
- A. K. Jagannatham, *Principles of Modern Wireless Communication Systems Theory and Practice*. McGraw Hill Education, 2017. ISBN: 978-1259029578

1.2   WiFi: IEEE 802.11-based wireless local area networks

Established by the Institute of Electrical and Electronics Engineers (IEEE), IEEE 802.11 is the most accepted wireless communications standard in the

---

[1]https://r2lab.inria.fr

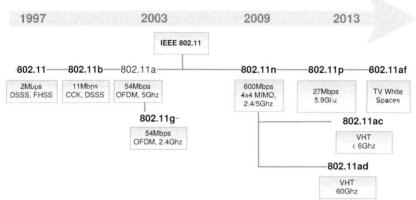

Figure 1.3: IEEE 802.11 modes.

world. WiFi technology, as it is most commonly known, is the Wireless Local Area Network (WLAN) technology based on IEEE 802.11, and it is a
trademark of the Wi-Fi Alliance. The reasons for the wide acceptance of this
pattern are diverse, but the main justification is cost-performance ratio.

As illustrated in Figure 1.3, there are several 802.11 standards, such as the
older 802.11b, 802.11a, and 802.11g versions, and other versions that may
be considered as newer, such as 802.11n, 802.11ac, 802.11p, and so on. In
general, the standards defined for 802.11 operate on two main frequencies:
2.4 GHz or 5 GHz. In the example given by Figure 1.4, it can be seen how
the 802.11b standard defines 13 channels on the 2.4 GHz band at 2.4835 Ghz,
allocating 22 MHz for each channel, with a spacing of 5 MHz among them.
With this arrangement, only channels 1, 6 and 11 can operate without band
overlap.

The Bit Error Rate (BER), which is a requirement to be fulfilled in the system
design, can be determined by knowing the modulation scheme, the type of
encoding and the signal-to-noise ratio (SNR). It is known that an increase in
transmitter power results in a higher SNR and a consequent decrease in BER.
Obviously, power cannot be increased indefinitely, due to interference and to
power limitations in the transmitter itself.

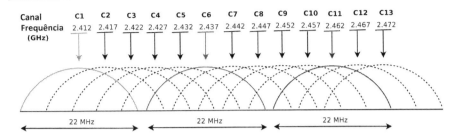

Figure 1.4: IEEE 802.11b channels. Source: adapted from [3] (CC BY 2.0)

Table 1.1: Comparing IEEE 802.11 modes.

Protocol	Freq. (GHz)	Bandwidth (MHz)	Internal Signal Range	External Signal Range
802.11	2.4	20	20 m / 66 ft	100 m / 330 ft
802.11a	3.7/ 5	20	35 m / 115 ft	120 m / 390 ft
802.11b	2.4	20	35 m / 115 ft	140 m / 460 ft
802.11g	2.4	20	38 m / 125 ft	140 m / 460 ft
802.11n	2.4/5	20 - 40	70 m / 230 ft	250 m / 820 ft
802.11ac	5	20/40/80/160	35 m / 115 ft	n/d
802.11ad	60	2,160	60 m / 200 ft	100 m / 300 ft
802.11ay	60	8000	60 m / 200 ft	1000 m / 3000 ft

Table 1.1 compares different 802.11 standards in terms of operating frequency, channel bandwidth and coverage radius estimates in indoor and outdoor environments. Table 1.2 compares 802.11n and 802.11ac, two of the newer standards that incorporate recent advances in wireless communications, such as spatial flows based on MIMO (Multiple Input Multiple Output).

The 802.11 architecture consists primarily of an access point and a number of wireless stations (clients). In this case, the architecture is defined as Basic Service Set (BSS), or infrastructure mode. In contrast, 802.11 networks composed of only wireless stations (clients) are referred to as Independent Basic Service Set (IBSS) or ad-hoc mode. The graphical representations of these two architectures (or modes of operation) are illustrated in Figures 1.5 e 1.6.

Table 1.2: IEEE 802.11n and IEEE 802.11ac comparison.

	IEEE 802.11n	IEEE 802.11ac
Frequency	2.4 GHz & 5 GHz	5 GHz
MIMO	Single User (SU)	Multi User (MU)
Spatial Flows	4	8
Taxa PHY	600 Mbps	6.9 Gbps
Channel Width	20 or 40 MHz	20, 40, 80, 80-80, 160 MHz
Modulation	64 QAM	256 QAM
Flow rate MAC*	390 Mbps	4.49 Gbps

*Assuming 65 % MAC efficiency and the highest rate of MCS
(*Modulation and Coding Scheme*)

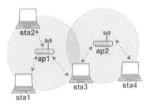

Figure 1.5: infrastructure.　　　　Figure 1.6: ad hoc.

As is true with Ethernet devices, each 802.11 wireless device has a 6-byte MAC address stored on the network interface card. It is through the wireless network interface that stations can associate with an access point or even other client stations before receiving or sending 802.11 frames.

Because wireless networks do not have the physical means to prevent collisions, these do happen even with the most advanced wireless technologies. While the IEEE 802 standards for Ethernet family cabling enable Collision Detection (CD), wireless networks have no means to detect a collision. The strategy adopted by the 802.11 standards to handle wireless access control is known as Carrier Sense Multiple Access with Collision Avoidance (CSMA/CA).

When the CSMA/CA method is used, each station informs about its own transmission intent and the associated time for Collision Avoidance (CA). The stations, which are equipped with wireless interfaces, listen to the medium using wireless interfaces to verify the presence of signals (signal level at

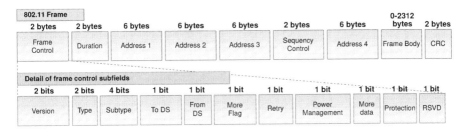

Figure 1.7: IEEE 802.11 frame header.

the carrier frequency) and wait until the medium is clear before transmitting. These mechanisms are known as Request to Send (RTS) and Clear to Send (CTS).

Despite the similarities between Ethernet frames and 802.11 frames, there are several fields that are specific to wireless links. The fields in the 802.11 table are shown in Figure 1.7. The numbers above each field in the frame represent their lengths in bytes, while the numbers above each of the sub-fields in the frame control field represent the lengths of the sub-fields in bits.

Although we do not go into detail about the function of each of the fields and sub-fields belonging to frame 802.11, it is advisable to know about them even if superficially. These fields may be useful for further exploration of some of the tutorials that will be presented throughout this book.

The future of WiFi

Although wireless networks are very important, there are still structural barriers that prevent their innovation, even with regard to WiFi itself. Furthermore, large wireless infrastructure is not completely accessible because there are restrictions on its use or authentication requirements. Namely, the issue here is not to open access to wireless networks completely and freely, but to allow users to connect to multiple networks (preserving security and quality standards), thus opening up a huge capacity for coverage and enabling continuous innovation, as proposed by [20].

Nevertheless, there are already several studies on vehicular networks and also the Internet of Things that use WiFi in their methods. Many of them, of course, provide only suggestions for improvements that may advance 802.11 in the future. Yet it is not for nothing that researchers already speak of 802.11ax, an evolution of 802.11ac that promises to connect more devices with higher baud rates than its predecessor.

Among the proposals for improvements and advancements in wireless networks and especially WiFi, is the concept of software-defined wireless networks, which also promises significant progress by constructing a new idea of connectivity. Therefore, along with the concept of software-defined wireless networks, this book will present a series of tutorials that will explore various cases involving Mininet-WiFi. Mininet-WiFi is the wireless emulator that we will use extensively throughout this book. It was developed with the aim of providing an environment capable of supporting research on wireless networks and software-defined wireless networks, enabling innovations to be developed for the most diverse wireless technologies.

- Matthew S. Gast. *802.11 Wireless Networks: The Definitive Guide.* O'Reilly Media, 2005. ISBN-13: 978-0596100520
- Matthew S. Gast. *802.11ac: A Survival Guide: Wi-Fi at Gigabit and Beyond.* O'Reilly Media (Edição: 2), 2013. ISBN-13: 978-1449343149
- Jim Geier, *Designing and Deploying 802.11 Wireless Networks: A Practical Guide to Implementing 802.11n and 802.11ac Wireless Networks For Enterprise-Based Applications.* Cisco Press, 2015. ISBN-13: 978-1587144301
- IEEE 802.11 Wireless Local Area Networks. The Working Group for WLAN Standards. Available at: http://www.ieee802.org/11/

1.3 Software-defined wireless networking

Software-defined wireless networking (SDWN) [5, 11] is an approach that allows centralized control of the network through the use of programs that do not necessarily have to be located in access points. Thus, rules defined by these programs (commonly known as controllers) dictate the behavior of the network. The principles of SDWN, which separate the control plane from the data plane, are very similar to those of software-defined networks (SDN) [12].

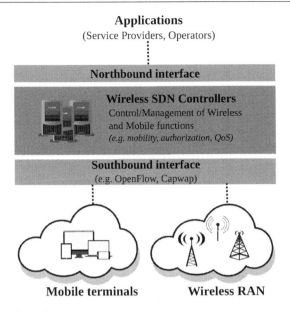

Figure 1.8: High-level and generic architecture for SDWN. Source: Adapted from [18]

The software-defined approach allows network administrators to specify network behavior in a logical and centralized way. To do so, they use programs provided by control platforms that implement southbound interfaces on network devices such as switches. In this context, the OpenFlow protocol [15] is the most popular southbound interface. However, there are other viable interfaces, such as CAPWAP [22], FORCES [7], NETCONF [8], etc.

Due to the increased interest of mobile operators [2, 19], mainly in Network Function Virtualization (NFV) [10], SDWN has become a branch of software-defined networks of considerable interest to the scientific community. The separation between the control plane and the data plane is not new in the history of wireless networks. The IETF standardized both the LWAPP (Lightweight Access Point Protocol) and the CAPWAP (Control and Provisioning of Wireless Access Points) many years ago by issuing RFC5412 [4] and RFC4564 [22], respectively - even before the development of software-defined networks and the OpenFlow protocol.

Many companies use wireless network management systems by means of protocols such as LWAPP and CAPWAP. LWAPP defines message control for configuration, authentication and other operations, while CAPWAP is based on LWAPP and allows a controller to manage different access points.

The number of studies on software-defined wireless networks has grown significantly in recent years. It is worth reading [11] for a more comprehensive survey, in addition to some software projects, such as: OpenRoads [23], Odin [21], OpenRF [13], Ethanol [17]. Architectures such as CloudMac [6] and Chandelle [16] use CAPWAP in their code. CloudMac describes wireless network management protocols, such as CAPWAP, as difficult to be configured with new features, since access point controllers that use CAPWAP are mostly proprietary systems. Chandelle, on the other hand, proposes a migration between smooth and fast access points using SDN/OpenFlow, but faces integration issues with regard to traditional switches and CAPWAP.

 It is important to mention that there is an open source implementation of the CAPWAP protocol that is compatible with RFC 4515 and RFC 4516, called OpenCAPWAP [1], whose development started in 2015 (https://github.com/vollero/openCAPWAP).

The benefits of integrating wireless networks with OpenFlow generally involve centralized management and monitoring, unified policies, greater scheduling, and better control of wireless functions.

Taking into account these benefits and the limitations associated with CAPWAP, which is likely to be a more robust but closed-source solution, some questions are unavoidable: *"Is CAPWAP compatible with SDWN?"*, *"How to improve the OpenFlow specification, so that it supports centralized management of wireless networks? Or even, could you extend it to wireless networks?"*, *"Are new approaches needed?"* or *"How much could be recycled from the existing infrastructure?"*.

- L. E. Li, Z. M. Mao and J. Rexford, *Toward Software-Defined Cellular Networks*. European Workshop on Software Defined Networking (EWSDN), 2012.
- A. Gudipati et al., *SoftRAN: software defined radio access network*. Proceedings of Hot topics in software defined networking (HotSDN). 2013.
- C. J. Bernardos et al., *An architecture for software defined wireless networking*. IEEE Wireless Communications. 2014.
- T. Chen et al., *Software defined mobile networks: concept, survey, and research directions*, IEEE Communications Magazine. 2015.
- Mao Yang et al., *Software-Defined and Virtualized Future Mobile and Wireless Networks: A Survey*. Mob. Netw. Appl. 2015.
- I. T. Haque and N. Abu-Ghazaleh, *Wireless Software Defined Networking: A Survey and Taxonomy*, in IEEE Communications Surveys & Tutorials. 2016.
- A. Abdelaziz et al. *On Software-Defined Wireless Network (SDWN) Network Virtualization: Challenges and Open Issues*. Computer Journal. 2017.
- Linux Foundation's Open Networking Foundation (ONF) SDN Wireless Transport. Available at: https://www.opennetworking.org/tag/wireless-transport/

1.4 Mininet-WiFi

Network emulation has been widely used in performance evaluation, protocol testing and debugging, as well as in a variety of research on computer network architectures. A researcher typically has several possible methods to evaluate and validate research data and network protocols, as well as perform analyses, among other operations.

Simulators, emulators and testbeds are the main evaluation tools that help researchers in their tasks. Still, regarding their practical applications, all these evaluation tools are very different in their degree of abstraction. Some of the experimental platforms that can be used for experimentation with wireless networks are shown in Figure 1.9. In this research field, the emulation of wireless networks - which has peculiar characteristics, especially compared with emulators for wired networks - has to implement node mobility, signal propagation, among other features, to allow experiments with environments that have interference, signal attenuation, etc.

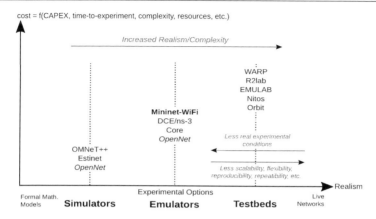

Figure 1.9: Experimental platforms for wireless networks. Source: Adapted from [9].

We will not go into detail about the differences between experimental platforms, but we can highlight two important features of Mininet-WiFi: (i) it allows the use of third-party tools without modifications to the source code of these tools, and (ii) it uses the actual network protocol stack.

Mininet-WiFi is an emulator for wireless networks that was extended from Mininet, a well-known emulator to researchers working in the field of software-defined networks. Mininet-WiFi has native WiFi support, but other wireless networking technologies can also be simulated in experiments using it. With Mininet-WiFi, the user can virtualize stations and access points and also use existing Mininet nodes such as hosts, switches and OpenFlow controllers. Consequently, Mininet-WiFi also enables the processing of packages using the OpenFlow protocol, an important solution for SDN.

 SoftMAC is a term used to describe a type of wireless network interface in which the MAC Layer Management Entity (MLME), for example, is expected to be managed using software. Mac80211 is a driver API for SoftMAC.

Mininet-WiFi is developed based on the Mininet code and the most used WiFi *driver* for Linux systems, *SoftMac*. With Mininet-WiFi, the user can choose to use the old Mininet features independently or use the extensions implemented for Mininet-WiFi.

1.4.1 Architecture

The entire virtualization process of Mininet-WiFi works similarly to Mininet, i.e. it is based on processes that run on Linux network namespaces and virtual network interfaces (see Figure 1.10). Linux network namespaces are, in a logical sense, copies of the Linux operating system's network stack, which includes its own routes, firewall rules and network devices. They act as if they were real computers, with the same network properties that a physical computer can have.

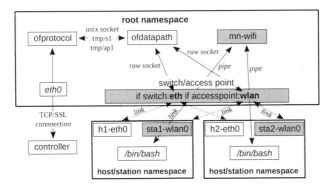

Figure 1.10: Mininet-WiFi architecture. Source: [9]

The behavior of wireless interfaces basically depends on the function they perform, such as, for instance, the case of stations and access points, whose interfaces operate in the managed or master modes, respectively. Just as with a real environment, the stations communicate with access points by a process called authentication and association. By default, each station has only one wireless interface, and more can be added if needed. Once connected to an access point, stations can communicate with traditional Mininet hosts, if they are also connected to the access point. Access points, on the other hand, are responsible for managing stations that are associated with them.

Conceptually, access points are the same entities as the Mininet switches, but equipped with WiFi network cards operating in master mode. Access points are virtualized in the *hostapd*[2] daemon, which basically uses virtual WiFi interfaces to provide access point capabilities. Details on the running environment of Mininet-WiFi are discussed below.

1.4.2 Components

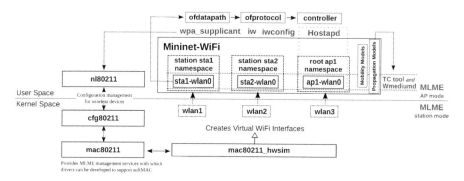

Figure 1.11: Main components of Mininet-WiFi. Source: [9]

The components comprising the Mininet-WiFi architecture are shown in Figure 1.11. Communication among them occurs as follows: during its initialization, the module called *mac80211_hwsim*, responsible for the virtualization of WiFi network cards, is loaded with the number of virtual wireless interfaces required for all nodes previously defined by the user. Located in the kernel space of the Linux operating system, all features supported by *mac80211_hwsim* come from mac80211, a framework based on *SoftMAC* that developers use to write drivers for wireless devices.

Also in the kernel space is *cfg80211*, which is an 802.11 heap configuration API for Linux systems. Its configuration is done by running *nl80211*, which also performs the interaction between kernel and user spaces.

The main network applications used by Mininet-WiFi are in the user space. Among them is *hostapd*, whose function is to provide access point services;

---

[2]Hostapd (**H**ost **A**ccess **P**oint **D**aemon) is a user-level software capable of launching a wireless network interface on access points and authentication servers.

the TC and Wmediumd programs, which will be described below; *iw*, *iwconfig* and *wpa_supplicant*. The latter is used for, among other tasks, WPA/WPA2 authentication.

Interacting with the emulation environment
Mininet-WiFi also maintains the same interaction structure as Mininet. E.g., commands such as those shown below can be used, respectively, for connectivity tests or to measure th bandwidth between two nodes. If you are already familiar with Mininet, this is certainly nothing new.

```
mininet-wifi> sta1 ping sta2
mininet-wifi> iperf sta1 sta2
```

In addition to these, other commands exclusive to Mininet-WiFi can be used for a better experience with the WiFi environment, such as the ones described below:

```
mininet-wifi> sta1 iw dev sta1-wlan0 scan
mininet-wifi> sta1 iw dev sta1-wlan0 connect ssid-ap1
```

These commands allow you to scan WiFi networks and connect to one of them, respectively. Scripts such as *iw*, the command used above, are natively supported by most Linux operating systems and have not been ported or modified to work on Mininet-WiFi. Mininet-WiFi can execute any command and/or program that runs on Linux distributions, such as Ubuntu.

• Ramon dos Reis Fontes, Samira Afzal, Samuel Brito, Mateus Santos, Christian Esteve Rothenberg. *Mininet-WiFi: Emulating Software-Defined Wireless Networks*. In 2nd International Workshop on Management of SDN and NFV Systems 2015. Barcelona, Spain, Nov. 2015. [9]

Level: beginner

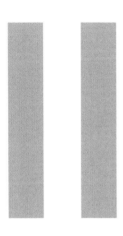

2. Beginner

In this chapter we introduce Mininet-WiFi and all features supported by this emulator, highlighting critical information necessary to understand the tutorials explored throughout this book. We begin by discussing all steps needed to get Mininet-WiFi up and running on your computer.

2.1 Downloading and installing Mininet-WiFi

The Mininet-WiFi source code is a *Git repository* publicly available on *Github*. Git is an amazing open source system, capable of handling the distributed version control of any given project, in this case the Mininet-WiFi project. It was devised by Linus Torvalds[1] himself as a means of helping the development, at the time, of a tiny project called Linux.

To ease the searching and following-up of projects managed by Git, developers usually share their Git repository on Github, a platform for creating, managing, further distributing and interacting with open-source projects. This means

---

[1] github.com/torvalds

that the life cycle of a project can be easily analyzed by contributors through Github, which keeps any file's modification history since its origin. In this book we only use the basic concepts of the Git system. For more information about Git and Github, please refer to *<git-scm.com>* and *<github.com/>*.

To obtain Mininet-WiFi's source code and install it, you will need to perform a process called cloning, in which all the information pertaining to a project is downloaded to your computer. Since Mininet-WiFi is a Git repository on Github, its cloning is carried out using the Git system.

After this brief introduction to Git and Github, you can clone the Mininet-WiFi source code by using the following command line, which consists of the instruction git clone followed by a link to Mininet-Wifi's Github repository.

```
~$ git clone https://github.com/intrig-unicamp/mininet-wifi
```

 Mininet-WiFi relies on Linux Kernel components to function properly. Of the different Linux distributions that can be used to this end, we recommend Ubuntu, since Mininet-WiFi was extensively tested on it.

In the link to Mininet-WiFi's repository, *intrig-unicamp* refers to the profile or organization where the repository is located on Github. *mininet-wifi*, in turn, is the name of the repository where the source code is deposited.

 If you do not have *git*, you can install it using the sudo apt install git command.

Once the clone is complete, a directory named *<mininet-wifi>* should be created. Since the cloning was done from the user's directory, the Mininet-WiFi source code should be located at *</home/your_username/mininet-wifi>*, or simply *<~/mininet-wifi>*.

Now you need to install Mininet-WiFi. To do so, you will need to access the created directory and execute the sudo util/install.sh command, as follows.

```
~$ cd mininet-wifi
~/mininet-wifi$ sudo util/install.sh -Wlnfv6
```

 Further information on the *Wlnfv6* parameters can be found on the Mininet-WiFi source code page on Github.

Alternatively, you can also use the virtual machine available on the source page. To ensure that the virtual machine has the latest version of Mininet-WiFi, you must use the commands below.

```
~/mininet-wifi$ git pull
~/mininet-wifi$ sudo make install
```

 Capturing the code through the git clone command ensures that the source code will always contain the latest updates implemented for Mininet-WiFi.

Even if you already have Mininet-WiFi and/or the virtual machine installed, the git pull command can be issued from the Mininet-WiFi directory at any time. This command will synchronize the code that is on your computer with the source code available in the Mininet-WiFi source code repository. By doing this, you will always have the latest version of Mininet-WiFi installed.

2.2 First steps to use Mininet-WiFi

In the following paragraphs, we will begin to understand how to use Mininet-WiFi.

First, we need to be aware of three commands: sudo mn --version, which prints the Mininet-WiFi version in use; sudo mn --help, which prints a help menu; and sudo mn -c, which is responsible for cleaning up poorly-made Mininet-WiFi executions. Remember this last command, because it will be very useful later on.

Mininet-WiFi can be started by running a very simple command, sudo mn --wifi. In addition to opening the Command Line Interface (CLI), this command will create a topology consisted of two stations connected to an access point via a wireless medium, as well as an SDN controller that is connected to the access point, as shown in Figure 2.1.

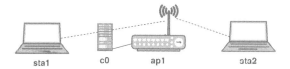

Figure 2.1: Simple topology.

```
~/mininet-wifi$ sudo mn --wifi
*** Creating network
*** Adding controller
*** Adding stations:
sta1 sta2
*** Adding access points:
ap1
*** Configuring wifi nodes...
*** Adding link(s):
(sta1, ap1) (sta2, ap1)
*** Configuring nodes
*** Starting controller(s)
c0
*** Starting switches and/or access points
ap1 ...
*** Starting CLI:
mininet-wifi>
```

 If you already know Mininet, you have probably already used the sudo mn command, which creates a simple topology with two hosts, one switch and one OpenFlow controller, connected by a wired medium.

 If you notice an error similar to the one below, it means that there is a controller or process already running on port 6653, the default port used by the most recent OpenFlow controllers. This problem can be solved using the sudo fuser -k 6653/tcp command, which will kill the process that is using port 6653. If the controller is running on port 6633, the same must be done with this port number.

```
Exception: Please shut down the controller which is running on port 6653:
Active Internet connections (servers and established)
tcp  0  0 0.0.0.0:6653   0.0.0.0:* LISTEN   2449/ovs-testcontro
tcp  0  0 127.0.0.1:55118   127.0.0.1:6653 TIME_WAIT   -
```

To identify the Mininet-WiFi CLI, just search for the text below:

```
mininet-wifi>
```

Within the CLI you can essentially use any network commands or programs. Additionally, it is also possible to list and execute a number of commands that have been implemented exclusively for Mininet-WiFi. The help command allows you to list available commands, as follows.

```
mininet-wifi> help
Documented commands (type help <topic>):
========================================
EOF       exit   iperf    nodes       pingpair     py     start  x
distance  gterm  iperfudp noecho      pingpairfull quit   stop   xterm
dpctl     help   links    pingall     ports        sh     switch
dump      intfs  net      pingallfull px           source time
```

Most of these commands already existed in Mininet and were kept for Mininet-WiFi. Only three new commands have been added to Mininet-WiFi: distance, start and stop. distance allows you to check the distance between two nodes, while start and stop allow you to pause and continue experiments that implement node mobility.

 This book will demonstrate the commands implemented for Mininet-WiFi, in addition to some others already implemented on Mininet.

Try using the nodes command to identify nodes that are part of the topology. Note that the nodes described by the nodes command are the same as those shown previously in Figure 2.1.
Note: Node c0 will be discussed later.

```
mininet-wifi> nodes
available nodes are:
ap1 c0 sta1 sta2
```

As previously mentioned, the sudo mn --wifi command creates a topology with stations that are connected through a wireless medium to an access point. This can be easily verified using wireless networking tools.

Although the sudo mn --wifi command creates an AP with an SSID called "my-ssid" operating on channel 1 (2412MHz), these values can also be customized. For instance, we will exit the Mininet-WiFi CLI with the exit command and then set up a new SSID and a new channel, as follows:

```
mininet-wifi> exit
~/mininet-wifi$ sudo mn --wifi --ssid=new-ssid --channel=10
```

Then try the following command.

```
mininet-wifi> sta1 iw dev sta1-wlan0 info
Interface sta1-wlan0
        ifindex 33
        wdev 0x1000000001
        addr 02:00:00:00:00:00
        ssid new-ssid
        type managed
        wiphy 16
        channel 10 (2457 MHz), width: 20 MHz (no HT), center1: 2457 MHz
        txpower 14.00 dBm
```

If you are new to wireless networking, especially on Linux operating systems, you might not have noticed, but you have just used a very common program in wireless networking environments, the *iw* tool. *iw* is a utility for wireless networks that is gradually replacing *iwconfig*. We will use it extensively throughout this book.

 iwconfig is certainly already installed on your system and you can also use it. For example, *sta1 iwconfig* will produce a similar result to the one shown previously by *iw*. Try running iwconfig --help for more information on how to use it.

With respect to the command that we have just used, the *info* parameter brings up information about the association (or no association) between nodes. It is noticeable that sta1 is associated with an access point with a SSID *new-ssid*

that also operates on channel 10, exactly as defined by the command.

Additionally, using the *link* parameter instead of *info* allows the user to obtain the signal level perceived by the node and the *bitrate*, in addition to transmitted and received packets, among other data.

```
mininet-wifi> sta1 iw dev sta1-wlan0 link
Connected to 02:00:00:00:02:00 (on sta1-wlan0)
    SSID: new-ssid
    freq: 2457
    RX: 1241 bytes (22 packets)
    TX: 93 bytes (2 packets)
    signal: -36 dBm
    tx bitrate: 1.0 MBit/s

    bss flags:          short-slot-time
    dtim period:        2rendering this PDF.

    beacon int:         100
```

Now, let us use the *ping* command to verify the connectivity between sta1 and sta2.

```
mininet-wifi> sta1 ping -c1 sta2
PING 10.0.0.2 (10.0.0.2) 56(84) bytes of data.
64 bytes from 10.0.0.2: icmp_seq=1 ttl=64 time=0.380 ms

--- 10.0.0.2 ping statistics ---
1 packets transmitted, 1 received, 0% packet loss, time 0ms
rtt min/avg/max/mdev = 0.380/0.380/0.380/0.000 ms
```

The command shows that there is communication between the two nodes in question, since it also displays a response time in milliseconds belonging to sta2(*ms*). It is important to note that because Mininet-WiFi is an emulation platform capable of emulating several nodes, it is necessary to define in the CLI the source node that will be responsible, in practice, for issuing a given command.

 The -c1 parameter used with the *ping* command means that only one ICMP packet will be sent. Otherwise, sta1 will send endless ICMP packets.

Thus, as the *ping* command needs a target node - which can be either a name or an IP address -, sta2's destination can also be replaced by its IP address. As can be seen below, the IP address that identifies sta2 is 10.0.0.2/8.

```
mininet-wifi> sta2 ip addr
1: lo: <LOOPBACK,UP,LOWER_UP> mtu 65536 qdisc noqueue state UNKNOWN group
 ↪  default qlen 1000
    link/loopback 00:00:00:00:00:00 brd 00:00:00:00:00:00
    inet 127.0.0.1/8 scope host lo
       valid_lft forever preferred_lft forever
    inet6 ::1/128 scope host
       valid_lft forever preferred_lft forever
34: sta2-wlan0: <BROADCAST,MULTICAST,UP,LOWER_UP> mtu 1500 qdisc htb state
 ↪  UP group default qlen 1000
    link/ether 02:00:00:00:01:00 brd ff:ff:ff:ff:ff:ff
    inet 10.0.0.2/8 scope global sta2-wlan0
       valid_lft forever preferred_lft forever
    inet6 fe80::ff:fe00:100/64 scope link
       valid_lft forever preferred_lft forever
```

Alternatively, you can also open different terminals for each node and issue commands as if they were being sent directly to a computer, exactly as it happens in the real world (see Figure 2.2). For example, the following command will open two terminals, one for sta1 and another for sta2. Once there is a terminal for each node, it will no longer be necessary to indicate which one is the origin, as explained in the previous paragraph.

```
mininet-wifi> xterm sta1 sta2
```

 Xterm may not work as expected if there is no GUI enabled on your operating system.

Now, we will perform a few routines and exclusive actions of the wireless environment. To begin, we will disconnect sta1 from ap1 and confirm the disassociation by issuing the following command:

```
mininet-wifi> sta1 iw dev sta1-wlan0 disconnect
mininet-wifi> sta1 iw dev sta1-wlan0 link
      Not connected.
```

So let us try a new *ping* between sta1 and sta2.

```
mininet-wifi> sta1 ping -c1 sta2
PING 10.0.0.2 (10.0.0.2) 56(84) bytes of data.
From 10.0.0.1 icmp_seq=1 Destination Host Unreachable

--- 10.0.0.2 ping statistics ---
1 packets transmitted, 0 received, +1 errors, 100% packet loss, time 0ms
```

As you can see, station sta1 is no longer associated with access point ap1, so it would be logically impossible to perform any kind of communication with sta2.

Now, we will connect sta1 again to the ap1 access point and confirm the association.

```
mininet-wifi> sta1 iw dev sta1-wlan0 connect new-ssid
mininet-wifi> sta1 iw dev sta1-wlan0 link
Connected to 02:00:00:00:02:00 (on sta1-wlan0)
        SSID: new-ssid
        freq: 2457
        RX: 370 bytes (9 packets)
        TX: 202 bytes (3 packets)
        signal: -36 dBm
        tx bitrate: 6.0 MBit/s

        bss flags:      short-slot-time
        dtim period:    2
        beacon int:     100
```

Figure 2.2: Executing xterm.

And then we will try a new *ping* between sta1 and sta2. The *ping* command should run successfully, as follows.

```
mininet-wifi> sta1 ping -c1 sta2
PING 10.0.0.2 (10.0.0.2) 56(84) bytes of data.
64 bytes from 10.0.0.2: icmp_seq=1 ttl=64 time=1011 ms

--- 10.0.0.2 ping statistics ---
1 packets transmitted, 1 received, 0% packet loss, time 0ms
rtt min/avg/max/mdev = 1011.206/1011.206/1011.206/0.000 ms
```

Another very useful operation for WiFi networks is scanning, which allows you to check which access points a certain station can see. For example, let us assume that the SSID of access point ap1 is unknown. In this case, the following command can be used to display ap1's SSID.

```
mininet-wifi> sta1 iw dev sta1-wlan0 scan
BSS 02:00:00:00:02:00(on sta1-wlan0) -- associated
    TSF: 1534710096681871 usec (17762d, 20:21:36)
    freq: 2457
    beacon interval: 100 TUs
    capability: ESS ShortSlotTime (0x0401)
    signal: -36.00 dBm
    last seen: 0 ms ago
    Information elements from Probe Response frame:
    SSID: new-ssid
    Supported rates: 1.0* 2.0* 5.5* 11.0* 6.0 9.0 12.0 18.0
    DS Parameter set: channel 1
    ERP: Barker_Preamble_Mode
    Extended supported rates: 24.0 36.0 48.0 54.0
    Extended capabilities:
            * Extended Channel Switching
            * Operating Mode Notification
```

2.3   Customizing topologies

Different topologies can be created in Mininet-WiFi, through simple commands or even by using scripts written in *Python*.

The topologies that can be created through commands are *single* and *linear*. To generate these two kinds of topologies, we will need to close Mininet-WiFi.

```
mininet-wifi> exit
```

So let us start with the *single* topology, which consists of one access point, ap1, and n stations associated with it. For example, the following command creates four stations, one access point and one SDN controller, as shown in Figure 2.3.

```
~/mininet-wifi$ sudo mn --wifi --topo single,4
```

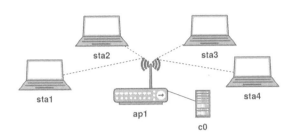

Figure 2.3: Single topology.

At this point, we can test the connectivity between all the nodes by issuing the pingall command, as follows.

```
mininet-wifi> pingall
*** Ping: testing ping reachability
sta1 -> *** sta1 : ('ping -c1  10.0.0.2',)
PING 10.0.0.2 (10.0.0.2) 56(84) bytes of data.
64 bytes from 10.0.0.2: icmp_seq=1 ttl=64 time=0.170 ms

--- 10.0.0.2 ping statistics ---
1 packets transmitted, 1 received, 0% packet loss, time 0ms
rtt min/avg/max/mdev = 0.170/0.170/0.170/0.000 ms
sta2 *** sta1 : ('ping -c1  10.0.0.3',)
PING 10.0.0.3 (10.0.0.3) 56(84) bytes of data.
64 bytes from 10.0.0.3: icmp_seq=1 ttl=64 time=0.121 ms

--- 10.0.0.3 ping statistics ---
1 packets transmitted, 1 received, 0% packet loss, time 0ms
rtt min/avg/max/mdev = 0.121/0.121/0.121/0.000 ms
sta3 *** sta1 : ('ping -c1  10.0.0.4',)
PING 10.0.0.4 (10.0.0.4) 56(84) bytes of data.
64 bytes from 10.0.0.4: icmp_seq=1 ttl=64 time=0.129 ms

--- 10.0.0.4 ping statistics ---
1 packets transmitted, 1 received, 0% packet loss, time 0ms
rtt min/avg/max/mdev = 0.129/0.129/0.129/0.000 ms
```

The other topology that can be created using commands is *linear*, which consists of n access points and n stations, in which each station is associated with one access point and all the access points are connected in a linear way. For example, the following command creates four access points, four stations, and one SDN controller, as shown in Figure 2.4.

```
~/mininet-wifi$ sudo mn --wifi --topo linear,4
```

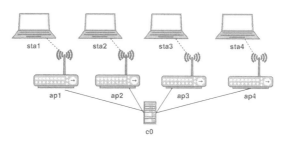

Figure 2.4: Linear topology.

The customization of topologies, on the other hand, is done by means of scripts that contain all the information about the topology as well as the configuration of its nodes. In the *</mininet-wifi/examples>* directory there is a wide variety of scripts that can be used as a basis for creating custom topologies.

It is always recommended that you check whether there is a script already developed for the scenario you want to work on. This helps you to create your own. Throughout this book we will use various scripts, which will certainly help in understanding how they can be customized.

2.4 Accessing node information

Now, let us learn how to get information from the nodes that make up a topology. To do so, we will create the simplest topology and add two new parameters: *position* and *wmediumd*. The *position* parameter will define initial positions for the nodes, while the *wmediumd* parameter will enable *wmediumd*, a wireless simulator that will be shown in 2.7.2.

```
~/mininet-wifi$ sudo mn --wifi --link=wmediumd --position
```

Then try issuing the `distance` command, as follows:

```
mininet-wifi> distance sta1 sta2
The distance between sta1 and sta2 is 100.00 meters
```

Now, check the position of `sta1` and `sta2`. Note that the x, y, and z axes are separated by commas.

```
mininet-wifi> py sta1.position
[1.0, 0.0, 0.0]

mininet-wifi> py sta2.position
[101.0, 0.0, 0.0]
```

As you can see, the initial positions were defined, and the `distance` command can be used to verify the distance between two nodes.

At this point a question surely may arise: what if a specific position for a node must be defined? In this case, there are two possible solutions: either through the Mininet-WiFi CLI or scripts. The example below shows the `setPosition()` method, which can be used with the CLI and scripts.

```
mininet-wifi> py sta1.setPosition('10,0,0')
```

Note that when a method implemented on the Mininet-WiFi source code is evoked by the CLI, the prefix *py* must always be used. In addition to `setPosition()`, other methods will be demonstrated throughout this book.

Now, let us check the newly defined position.

```
mininet-wifi> py sta1.position
[10.0, 0.0, 0.0]
```

In this case, the position is defined as: x=10, y=0 and z=0.

Various other data about a particular node can be obtained using the generic form *node.params* or *node.wintfs*, as shown below.

```
mininet-wifi> py sta1.params
{'wlan': ['sta1-wlan0'], 'ip': '10.0.0.1/8', 'ip6':
↪ '2001:0:0:0:0:0:0:1/64', 'channel': 1, 'mode': 'g'}
mininet-wifi> py sta1.wintfs
{0: <managed sta1-wlan0>}
```

Now, you can filter the desired information as follows.

```
mininet-wifi> py sta1.wintfs[0].freq
2.412
mininet-wifi> py sta1.wintfs[0].mode
g
mininet-wifi> py sta1.wintfs[0].txpower
14
mininet-wifi> py sta1.wintfs[0].range
62
mininet-wifi> py sta1.wintfs[0].antennaGain
5
```

wintfs[0] means that the information to be obtained comes from the first wireless interface. If the node has multiple interfaces, *wintfs[n]* - e.g. *wintfs[1]* to indicate the second interface and so on - can also be used.

2.5   OVSAP *versus* UserAP

Mininet-WiFi supports two types of access points that differ basically in the location where they are run. *OVSAP* or *OVSKernelAP* runs in the kernel space of the operating system, whereas the *UserAP* is executed in the user space. Additionally, you may prefer one over the other due to possible advantages, such as supported features and performance.

For example, some features may be supported by one and not by another. Until recently, *OVSAP* did not support *meter tables*, a type of table belonging to the OpenFlow protocol that is responsible for Quality of Service (QoS)-related operations, which was included in version 1.3 of this protocol. On the other hand, *UserAP* already supported it by then.

Another important issue is the possibility of running switches or access points in particular *network namespaces*. In this case, *OVS* does not support this feature natively yet, unlike *UserAP*, which supports it. What does that mean? Try using the following command.

```
~/mininet-wifi$ sudo mn --wifi
```

It allows you to view the interfaces of the ap1 access point.

```
mininet-wifi> ap1 ip link
1: lo: <LOOPBACK,UP,LOWER_UP> mtu 65536 qdisc noqueue state UNKNOWN mode
↪   DEFAULT group default qlen 1000
    link/loopback 00:00:00:00:00:00 brd 00:00:00:00:00:00
2: enp2s0: <NO-CARRIER,BROADCAST,MULTICAST,UP> mtu 1500 qdisc fq_codel
↪   state DOWN mode DEFAULT group default qlen 1000
    link/ether 84:7b:eb:fc:63:1a brd ff:ff:ff:ff:ff:ff
3: wlp1s0: <BROADCAST,MULTICAST,UP,LOWER_UP> mtu 1500 qdisc noqueue state
↪   UP mode DORMANT group default qlen 1000
    link/ether f8:da:0c:95:12:d3 brd ff:ff:ff:ff:ff:ff
4: docker0: <NO-CARRIER,BROADCAST,MULTICAST,UP> mtu 1500 qdisc noqueue
↪   state DOWN mode DEFAULT group default
    link/ether 02:42:04:ed:bc:24 brd ff:ff:ff:ff:ff:ff
5: br-7e51375c6c71: <NO-CARRIER,BROADCAST,MULTICAST,UP> mtu 1500 qdisc
↪   noqueue state DOWN mode DEFAULT group default
    link/ether 02:42:6f:43:07:ee brd ff:ff:ff:ff:ff:ff
6: hwsim0: <BROADCAST,MULTICAST> mtu 1500 qdisc noop state DOWN mode
↪   DEFAULT group default qlen 1000
    link/ieee802.11/radiotap 12:00:00:00:00:00 brd ff:ff:ff:ff:ff:ff
9: ap1-wlan1: <BROADCAST,MULTICAST,UP,LOWER_UP> mtu 1500 qdisc tbf master
↪   ovs-system state UP mode DEFAULT group default qlen 1000
    link/ether 02:00:00:00:02:00 brd ff:ff:ff:ff:ff:ff
10: ovs-system: <BROADCAST,MULTICAST> mtu 1500 qdisc noop state DOWN mode
↪   DEFAULT group default qlen 1000
    link/ether ee:99:70:bb:39:89 brd ff:ff:ff:ff:ff:ff
11: ap1: <BROADCAST,MULTICAST> mtu 1500 qdisc noop state DOWN mode DEFAULT
↪   group default qlen 1000
    link/ether 0a:94:5d:2c:8b:40 brd ff:ff:ff:ff:ff:ff
```

Note that a large number of network interfaces can be viewed, including those that, in practice, do not integrate the ap1 access point, such as the wireless and wired interfaces of the computer running Mininet-WiFi. This is the behavior observed when *OVS*, the default type of switch or access point for Mininet-WiFi, is being used.

Now, let us look at how *UserAP* behaves. To do so, run the following command.

```
~/mininet-wifi$ sudo mn --wifi --ap user --innamespace
```

 The –*innamespace* parameter was not used with OVS because it does not support this command yet. –*innamespace* is responsible for making the node run in its own *network namespace*, instead of the root network namespace.

After that, check the interfaces of the ap1 access point.

```
mininet-wifi> ap1 ip link
1: lo: <LOOPBACK> mtu 65536 qdisc noop state DOWN mode DEFAULT group
 ↪ default qlen 1000
   link/loopback 00:00:00:00:00:00 brd 00:00:00:00:00:00
2: ap1-eth0@if46: <BROADCAST,MULTICAST,UP,LOWER_UP> mtu 1500 qdisc noqueue
 ↪ state UP mode DEFAULT group default qlen 1000
   link/ether de:93:af:2c:68:a0 brd ff:ff:ff:ff:ff:ff link-netnsid 0
45: ap1-wlan1: <BROADCAST,MULTICAST,UP,LOWER_UP> mtu 1500 qdisc tbf state
 ↪ UP mode DEFAULT group default qlen 1000
   link/ether 02:00:00:00:02:00 brd ff:ff:ff:ff:ff:ff
```

As you can realize, the number of network interfaces has dropped considerably. The loopback interface was expected to appear among the results, in addition to the ap1-wlan1 interface, which is the wireless interface of the ap1 access point. The only interface that could be considered as unexpected would be the ap1-eth0 interface, which is the interface used to connect to the SDN controller.

Another relevant issue between *OVSAP* and *UserAP* is the performance. *UserAP*'s performance has significantly worsened since the releases of the newer versions of the Linux kernel. The reason? We confess not to have an answer to this question. However, we invite you to check this issue in practice.

The following command will run Mininet with *OVS* and test the throughput between nodes h1 and h2.

```
~/mininet-wifi$ sudo mn --test iperf
*** Iperf: testing TCP bandwidth between h1 and h2
*** Results: ['40.1 Gbits/sec', '40.0 Gbits/sec']
```

The following command runs Mininet with *UserSwitch* and measures the throughput between the same nodes, h1 and h2.

```
~/mininet-wifi$ sudo mn --switch=user --test iperf
*** Iperf: testing TCP bandwidth between h1 and h2
*** Results: ['171 Mbits/sec', '172 Mbits/sec']
```

If you are not able to execute the previous command, you need to start an SDN controller on another terminal and replace `--test iperf` by `--controller=remote`. Then, after starting the controller, run *iperf* on the Mininet-WiFi CLI as follows: `iperf h1 h2`.

You may be wondering: why *UserSwitch*? *UserAP* has been extended from Mininet's *UserSwitch*. So in practice, they are the same switch or access point. But back to the result, did you notice the difference between them? *UserSwitch* has much lower performance compared to OVS.

With respect to *UserAP* still, an example of its implementation is *Basic Open-Flow Software Switch (BOFUSS)*, a successor of *ofsoftswitch13*[2]. It has been employed in several studies and you may definitely want to use it at some point. *BOFUSS* promises to eliminate most performance-related issues.

 To install *BOFUSS*, just run `sudo util/install.sh -3f` from Mininet-WiFi's root directory.

2.6 Graphical User Interface (GUI)

For those who do not know *Python* or are new to Mininet-WiFi, currently there are two options for creating scripts in *Python* with the support of graphic interfaces: by using *Visual Network Descriptor (VND)* or *MiniEdit*.

2.6.1 Visual Network Descriptor

 Requirement(s): web server, php, flash player, visual network descriptor

Visual Network Descriptor, or simply VND, is a tool created for a master's work that is able to generate *Python* scripts for Mininet-WiFi via a web browser. Written predominantly in the *Flex* programming language, VND also includes

---

[2]`https://github.com/CPqD/ofsoftswitch13`

some instructions in PHP and XML.

Using VND is relatively simple. First you need to make a clone of its source code, which can be downloaded at https://github.com/ramonfontes/vnd, and follow the installation steps available on the source code page. In general terms, you must have a web server, PHP and Flash Player installed. Then just access it through your preferred web browser. If all goes well, a screen similar to the one shown in Figure 2.5 should appear.

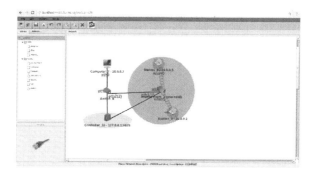

Figure 2.5: Visual Network Descriptor.

With VND open, you can use the mouse cursor to select the nodes that you want to include in the topology and their respective connections. You can also create settings for nodes and save the topology for later use. To generate scripts for Mininet-WiFi, just follow the *File->Export->Export to Mininet-WiFi* menu. A standard file with a .sh extension will be created; it consists of *Python* statements and can be executed as if it were a *Python* file.

For example, a script named *<mytopology.sh>* can be executed as follows.

```
~/mininet-wifi$ sudo python mytopology.sh
```

 Visual Network Descriptor:
https://youtu.be/KsoRMnDP_PA

2.6.2   MiniEdit

 Requirement(s): scripts only

Another alternative for creating topologies with graphics support is *MiniEdit*. Written in *Python*, *MiniEdit* was initially developed for Mininet and has been constantly upgraded to work with Mininet-WiFi. The goal of *MiniEdit*'s developers is to make all the features supported by Mininet-WiFi available on *MiniEdit*.

MiniEdit has a fairly simple user interface that features a screen with a line of tool icons on the left side of the window and a menu bar at the top. It comes already included in the Mininet-WiFi source code.

To use it, just run *<examples/miniedit.py>*.

```
~/mininet-wifi$ sudo python examples/miniedit.py
```

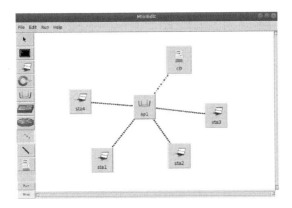

Figure 2.6: Miniedit.

After you run it, a screen similar to the one shown in Figure 2.6 should appear. With it you can add nodes supported by Mininet-WiFi and their respective settings, in addition to their links, of course. In the current version of *MiniEdit*, different types of scenarios are already supported, for example: *adhoc* and *mesh* networks, *WiFi-Direct*, Radius protocol, WPA, among other environments.

You might ask: what is the best alternative to work with GUI? *MiniEdit* or VND? You may want to use *MiniEdit*, since it is a part of Mininet-WiFi. There is also a tendency for VND to be gradually discontinued.

  MiniEdit and Mininet-WiFi:
https://youtu.be/j4JS4xxCrCA

2.6.3 Viewing 2D and 3D graphics

Viewing topologies by means of graphics is another feature that can be used in Mininet-WiFi. You can generate both 2D and 3D graphics. Nevertheless, there are situations where 3D graphics are very useful, such as surveys involving drones and satellites, since the representation of different levels of altitudes may be necessary.

Thus, given its importance, we will then understand how it is possible to generate 2D and 3D graphics on Mininet-WiFi. Initially we will learn to create the two types of graphics (2D and 3D) using the CLI.

The command below will generate a 2D topology.

```
~/mininet-wifi$ sudo mn --wifi --plot --position
```

While the following command will generate a 3D topology.

```
~/mininet-wifi$ sudo mn --wifi --plot3d --position
```

All scripts available in the *</examples>* directory - a Mininet-WiFi directory where you can find a wide variety of ready-to-run scripts - generate 2D graphics. If you choose to generate 3D graphics, simply make a small change in the code.

For example, let us take as an example *<position.py>*, available in the *</examples>* directory. This file contains the following content:

```
net.plotGraph(max_x=100, max_y=100)
```

As can be seen, only the x and y axes were defined and the resulting graph will be somewhat similar to the one shown in Figure 2.7. Therefore, to generate 3D graphics, simply add the z axis, which will produce something similar to what was shown in Figure 2.8.

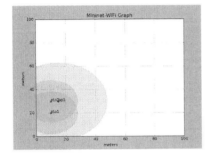

Figure 2.7: 2D Graphic.

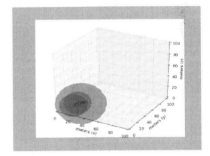

Figure 2.8: 3D Graphic.

```
net.plotGraph(max_x=100, max_y=100, max_z=100)
```

Optionally, minimum values for x, y and z axes can also be defined.

```
net.plotGraph(min_x=10, min_y=10, min_z=10, max_x=100, max_y=100,
↪  max_z=100)
```

 Graphics generated by Mininet-WiFi are supported by *matplotlib*, a data visualization library available in the *Python* programming language.

 Building 3D Graphic:
https://youtu.be/1MkIVOYBTss

2.7   Wireless network emulation

Wireless media emulation in Mininet-WiFi can be done in two ways: with TC[3] or Wmediumd[4]. Let us then understand how to use them and what are the differences between them.

2.7.1   TC (*Traffic Control*)

If Mininet-WiFi is running, quit it. Then start it again with the following command:

```
~/mininet-wifi$ sudo mn --wifi --position
```

Now, view the TC information on the Mininet-WiFi CLI:

```
mininet-wifi> ap1 tc qdisc
qdisc noqueue 0: dev lo root refcnt 2
qdisc pfifo_fast 0: dev enp2s0 root refcnt 2 bands 3
priomap  1 2 2 2 1 2 0 0 1 1 1 1 1 1 1 1
qdisc noqueue 0: dev wlp1s0 root refcnt 2
qdisc noqueue 0: dev docker0 root refcnt 2
qdisc tbf 2: dev ap1-wlan1 root refcnt 5 rate 54Mbit burst 14998b lat 1.0ms
qdisc pfifo 10: dev ap1-wlan1 parent 2:1 limit 1000p
```

The output that interests us is highlighted below:

```
qdisc tbf 2: dev ap1-wlan1 root refcnt 5
rate 54Mbit burst 14998b lat 1.0ms
```

In general terms, this output instructs ap1 to limit the bandwidth to up to 54 Mbits/s, which represents the maximum value that the IEEE 802.11g standard can nominally support. With this information it is easier to understand how TC works.

Considering that TC values are applied to stations and also that propagation models are supported by Mininet-WiFi, for a distance d between access point and station, there is always a received signal value, which can vary with the chosen propagation model. Then, as the node is moving to a new position, a new value for d is calculated and from this we obtain the received signal and

---
[3] https://en.wikipedia.org/wiki/Tc_(Linux)
[4] https://github.com/ramonfontes/wmediumd/

the bandwidth value that will be applied by TC to the wireless interface of the node.

In practice, the value applied by TC to ap1 does not change; instead, the values applied to the interfaces of the stations change. Thus, in an infrastructure environment we will always have two reference points for the calculation of *d*: the station and the access point. Two stations may be associated with the same access point, and different bandwidth values can be assigned to their interfaces: one for sta1 and another for sta2.

Now let us imagine a wireless ad hoc network with three stations. As a wireless network, we can say that this network consists of a non-infrastructure environment, which means that this topology does not have a central node, i.e. the access point. In this type of network the three stations can associate with each other, where, for example, sta1 can maintain association with sta2 and sta3. However, they only have one wireless interface, and thus are particularly difficult to control using TC.

What would be the reference point to calculate *d* for sta1, sta2 or sta3? Differently from an infrastructure network, where we have two reference points for the calculation of *d* - station and access point -, in a non-infrastructure network this does not occur. Thus, wireless *adhoc* and *mesh*, require the use of *Wmediumd*, which implements an ideal wireless medium simulator for these types of networks.

2.7.2 Wmediumd

The module responsible for virtualizing WiFi network cards on Mininet-WiFi, mac80211_hwsim, uses the same virtual medium for all its wireless nodes. This means that all nodes are internally within reach of each other and can be discovered by scanning, as we have done with *iw* previously. If the wireless interfaces need to be isolated from each other, the use of *Wmediumd* is recommended.

Wmediumd had been developed since 2011[5], but only in 2017 it was inte-

---

[5]https://github.com/jlopex/mac80211_hwsim

grated into Mininet-WiFi thanks to Patrick Große[6], the developer responsible for creating the first *Wmediumd* extension for Mininet-WiFi.

Unlike TC, which limits the bandwidth available to the interface, *Wmediumd* relies on a signal table[7] and manages the isolation of the interfaces in real time as data travels across the network.

2.7.3 TC *versus* Wmediumd in practice

Start Mininet-WiFi with the following command.

```
~/mininet-wifi$ sudo mn --wifi --topo single,3 --position --plot
```

This command will create three stations that will associate themselves with access point ap1. The --plot parameter will open a topology graph. More details on this parameter will be seen later.

Now, check the signal strength perceived by sta1 in relation to the ap1 access point by running the scan command.

```
mininet-wifi> sta1 iw dev sta1-wlan0 scan
BSS 02:00:00:00:03:00(on sta1-wlan0) -- associated
        TSF: 1536705774286475 usec (17785d, 22:42:54)
        freq: 2412
        beacon interval: 100 TUs
        capability: ESS ShortSlotTime (0x0401)
        signal: -36.00 dBm
        last seen: 0 ms ago
        Information elements from Probe Response frame:
        SSID: my-ssid
        Supported rates: 1.0* 2.0* 5.5* 11.0* 6.0 9.0 12.0 18.0
        DS Parameter set: channel 1
        ERP: Barker_Preamble_Mode
        Extended supported rates: 24.0 36.0 48.0 54.0
        Extended capabilities:
                * Extended Channel Switching
                * Operating Mode Notification
```

Also check the RSSI using the *wintfs* option:

---

[6]https://github.com/patgrosse
[7]https://github.com/ramonfontes/wmediumd/blob/mininet-wifi/tests/signal_table_ieee80211ax

```
mininet-wifi> py sta1.wintfs[0].rssi
-66.0
```

As you can see, there is a difference in the signals received by the iw scan and *wintfs* options. With iw the received signal was -36 dBm, whereas using wintfs it was -66 dBm. While TC is in use, it will not be possible to get any updated information about the signal strength, or any other data that depends on it, by using network commands, such as *iw*. Perhaps one of the few useful data to verify is whether the station sta1 is in fact associated with the access point ap1.

The *iw link* command can also be used for this, as follows.

```
mininet-wifi> sta1 iw dev sta1-wlan0 link
Connected to 02:00:00:00:03:00 (on sta1-wlan0)
SSID: my-ssid
freq: 2412
RX: 12486 bytes (236 packets)
TX: 805 bytes (9 packets)
signal: -36 dBm
tx bitrate: 18.0 MBit/s

bss flags:        short-slot-time
dtim period:      2
beacon int:       100
```

Now let us move sta1 and test the received signal again by performing a new scan.

```
mininet-wifi> py sta1.setPosition('250,250,0')
mininet-wifi> sta1 iw dev sta1-wlan0 scan
BSS 02:00:00:00:03:00(on sta1-wlan0)
        TSF: 1536706071142532 usec (17785d, 22:47:51)
        freq: 2412
        beacon interval: 100 TUs
        capability: ESS ShortSlotTime (0x0401)
        signal: -36.00 dBm
        last seen: 0 ms ago
        Information elements from Probe Response frame:
        SSID: my-ssid
        Supported rates: 1.0* 2.0* 5.5* 11.0* 6.0 9.0 12.0 18.0
        DS Parameter set: channel 1
        ERP: Barker_Preamble_Mode
        Extended supported rates: 24.0 36.0 48.0 54.0
        Extended capabilities:
```

```
* Extended Channel Switching
* Operating Mode Notification
```

Surprisingly, the signal remained the same as before, even when changing the position of sta1. In fact, ap1 should not even appear in the scan, as sta1 is no longer under the signal coverage of access point ap1. This shows that the TC really does not perceive the wireless medium, since even when the station is no longer within the signal coverage of the ap1 access point, it is still capable of seeing it.

Now, let us repeat what we did earlier by using *Wmediumd*.

```
~/mininet-wifi$ sudo mn --wifi --topo single,3 --link=wmediumd --position
↪ --plot
```

Then we perform the scan from sta1, change its position and repeat the scan.

```
mininet-wifi> sta1 iw dev sta1-wlan0 scan
BSS 02:00:00:00:03:00(on sta1-wlan0) -- associated
        TSF: 1536709235310507 usec (17785d, 23:40:35)
        freq: 2412
        beacon interval: 100 TUs
        capability: ESS ShortSlotTime (0x0401)
        signal: -67.00 dBm
        last seen: 0 ms ago
        Information elements from Probe Response frame:
        SSID: my-ssid
        Supported rates: 1.0* 2.0* 5.5* 11.0* 6.0 9.0 12.0 18.0
        DS Parameter set: channel 1
        ERP: Barker_Preamble_Mode
        Extended supported rates: 24.0 36.0 48.0 54.0
        Extended capabilities:
                * Extended Channel Switching
                * Operating Mode Notification
mininet-wifi> py sta1.setPosition('250,250,0')
mininet-wifi> sta1 iw dev sta1-wlan0 scan
```

As you can see, the signal strength perceived by sta1 was initially -67 dBm. However, when it went out of the signal range of access point ap1, there was a predicted change in the result. In addition to returning an expected signal value at the first moment, in the second the ap1 access point could not be reached, since ap1 was not able to reach sta1 anymore.

Using *wintfs* with *Wmediumd* is not recommended since some implementations of the latter for the calculation of the received signal were not transferred to Mininet-WiFi. In this case, it is always preferable to use *iw* or *iwconfig*.

2.8 Propagation model

Propagation models are mathematical models typically used by simulators and wireless network emulators to try to mimic the behavior of a wireless medium. In the literature, several propagation models have been proposed in order to support the different features of wireless media, such as varied environment types (indoor and outdoor), signal attenuation, interference, etc.

Mininet-WiFi currently supports the following propagation models: *Friis Propagation Loss Model*, *Log-Distance Propagation Loss Model* (default), *Log-Normal Shadowing Propagation Loss Model*, *International Telecommunication Union (ITU) Propagation Loss Model* and *Two-Ray Ground Propagation Loss Model*.

The correct choice of propagation model makes a big difference. For example, one of the variables used in propagation models is the exponent. The exponent is variable that will instruct the propagation model as to the testing environment, i.e. whether it is an indoor or outdoor environment, or whether it is an interference-free environment or not.

Specifying a propagation model is a simple task. The various Mininet-WiFi sample scripts will certainly support this task, especially *<propagationModel.py>*. In it you can find the function responsible for defining the propagation model and its parameters.

To demonstrate how the propagation model can affect the configuration of the nodes that make up the network, we will execute the following script.

```
~/mininet-wifi$ sudo python examples/propagationModel.py
```

Using the pre-defined propagation model, we can observe that the signal strength perceived by sta1 was around -79 dBm.

```
mininet-wifi> py sta1.wintfs[0].rssi
-79.0
```

On the other hand, after configuring the *free space* propagation model, the signal strength increased to approximately -47 dBm. If you did not find the -79 dBm and -47 dBm values, do not worry. What matters is the value obtained after setting up the propagation model. This should be higher than the previously noted values.

The propagation model can be modified as follows:

from:

```
net.setPropagationModel(model="logDistance", exp=4)
```

to:

```
net.setPropagationModel(model="friis")
```

Then, check the RSSI after running the modified script.

```
mininet-wifi> py sta1.wintfs[0].rssi
-47.0
```

Another relevant change you can see is related to the range of the access point. Certainly the new range of access point ap1 is now much larger than the previously observed one.

 <propagationModel.py> does not use *Wmediumd*, so if it is necessary to obtain the signal strength it should always be obtained using the *wintfs* command.

The new signal range value evidences the importance of choosing the correct propagation model for the scenario on which it is necessary to work. The new signal strength, which is higher than the previous one, also shows the behavior of the *free space* propagation model, since *free space* does not take into account any kind of interference or barrier that could attenuate the signal.

It is important to note that in addition to the exponent discussed above, there are other parameters that may be unique or not in relation to each model. You can find more information about the supported models and their parameters on Mininet-WiFi's web page[8].

2.8.1 Providing more realism

Some propagation models have no signal variation over time. This means that if we check the signal strength of a particular node, the perceived signal strength will always be the same. However, as we all know, the wireless medium is not constant and many factors can affect the perceived signal strength.

Therefore, in cases where the variation in signal strength is important and you need to represent what happens in the real world with greater fidelity, it is necessary to set up the *fading_coefficient*, which produces signal attenuation over time.

To check the effect caused by *fading* in practice, let us run the following code.

```
~/mininet-wifi$ sudo python examples/wmediumd_interference.py
```

Now we are able to verify the signal strength variation perceived by a given station through *iw*, as below. Notice that as *<wmediumd_interference.py>* uses *Wmediumd*, the signal strength can be obtained by running either *iw* or *iwconfig*.

```
mininet-wifi> sta1 iw dev sta1-wlan0 link
Connected to 02:00:00:00:03:00 (on sta1-wlan0)
SSID: new-ssid
freq: 5180
RX: 6901 bytes (124 packets)
TX: 712 bytes (8 packets)
signal: -65 dBm
tx bitrate: 12.0 MBit/s

bss flags:       short-slot-time
dtim period:     2
```

---

[8]http://mininet-wifi.github.io/

```
beacon int:        100

mininet-wifi> sta1 iw dev sta1-wlan0 link
Connected to 02:00:00:00:03:00 (on sta1-wlan0)
SSID: new-ssid
freq: 5180
RX: 8827 bytes (165 packets)
TX: 800 bytes (9 packets)
signal: -62 dBm
tx bitrate: 12.0 MBit/s

bss flags:         short-slot-time
dtim period:       2
beacon int:        100
```

As you can see, the signal strength perceived by sta1 was initially -65 dBm and then switched to -62 dBm later on. This variation is expected to happen whenever the received signal level is checked. This is a variation that occurs in a random fashion while also respecting the interval defined by the *fading* parameter.

 Try changing the *fading* value and check the result. The higher the *fading* value, the greater the signal variation.

 All propagation models supported by Mininet-WiFi can be found in <*mn_wifi/propagationModels.py*>. Should you want to implement new propagation models, you will need to include them in this file.

2.9 Distance *versus* received signal

In addition to the throughput, the distance variation will also impact the signal strength received from the nodes. Obviously, the more distant the source and destination are, the worse the perceived signal should be. This is due to signal attenuation.

We have already seen in 2.2 how we can visualize the signal strength perceived by a node. Let us use, then, the same command to observe the perceived signal strength from different positions. To do so, run <*wmediumd_interference.py*>.

```
~/mininet-wifi$ sudo python examples/wmediumd_interference.py
```

Then check the received signal.

```
mininet-wifi> sta1 iw dev sta1-wlan0 link
Connected to 02:00:00:00:03:00 (on sta1-wlan0)
    SSID: new-ssid
    freq: 5180
    RX: 9142 bytes (184 packets)
    TX: 88 bytes (2 packets)
    signal: -64 dBm
    tx bitrate: 6.0 MBit/s

    bss flags:        short-slot-time
    dtim period:      2
    beacon int:       100
```

Now, let us use the distance command to view the distance between sta1
and ap1.

```
mininet-wifi> distance sta1 ap1
The distance between sta1 and ap1 is 11.18 meters
```

As you can see, the distance between them is just over 11 meters, and the
signal level perceived by sta1 was -64 dBm. So let us change the position of
sta1 in order to reduce the distance from access point ap1 and check again
the signal strength received by sta1.

```
mininet-wifi> py sta1.setPosition('40,40,0')
mininet-wifi> distance sta1 ap1
The distance between sta1 and ap1 is 26.93 meters
mininet-wifi> sta1 iw dev sta1-wlan0 link
Connected to 02:00:00:00:03:00 (on sta1-wlan0)
    SSID: new-ssid
    freq: 5180
    RX: 176746 bytes (4379 packets)
    TX: 1668 bytes (19 packets)
    signal: -79 dBm
    tx bitrate: 18.0 MBit/s

    bss flags:        short-slot-time
    dtim period:      2
    beacon int:       100
```

We can see that after changing the position, the distance increased and consequently the signal level decreased from -64 dBm to -79 dBm. This may be

a simple and obvious conclusion; however, the steps we have just taken aid greatly in the teaching and learning process.

 • Ramon dos Reis Fontes, Mohamed Mahfoudi, Walid Dabbous, Thierry Turletti, Christian Esteve Rothenberg. *How far can we go? Towards Realistic Software-Defined Wireless Networking Experiments.* In The Computer Journal (Special Issue on Software Defined Wireless Networks), 2017.

2.10   Modifying *bitrate*

Bitrate refers to the rate of data transmission supported for a given moment. Wi-Fi devices are able to adjust their Modulation and Coding Scheme according to the received signal level. In practice, the more complex the modulation scheme is, the more bits can be transmitted. In contrast, they also become more sensitive to interference and noise, and hence require a cleaner channel.

We will use *iw* to modify bit rates. To do so, consider using <*wmediumd_interference.py*> one more time.

```
~/mininet-wifi$ sudo python examples/wmediumd_interference.py
```

Next, let us do some simple tests and note the difference in the bandwidth values obtained for different bitrates.

First, run *iperf* without changing the bitrate values.

```
mininet-wifi> iperf sta1 sta2
*** Iperf: testing TCP bandwidth between sta1 and sta2
*** Results: ['14.3 Mbits/sec', '14.4 Mbits/sec']
```

Then look at the current bitrate. As you can see below, the bitrate value was 54 Mbits/s.

```
mininet-wifi> sta1 iw dev sta1-wlan0 link
Connected to 02:00:00:00:03:00 (on sta1-wlan0)
        SSID: new-ssid
        freq: 5180
        RX: 581186 bytes (7475 packets)
```

```
TX: 19278284 bytes (12610 packets)
signal: -64 dBm
tx bitrate: 54.0 MBit/s

bss flags:         short-slot-time
dtim period:       2
beacon int:        100
```

Now, change the bitrate and re-measure the bandwidth.

```
mininet-wifi> sta1 iw dev sta1-wlan0 set bitrates legacy-5 6 9
mininet-wifi> iperf sta1 sta2
*** Iperf: testing TCP bandwidth between sta1 and sta2
*** Results: ['5.87 Mbits/sec', '5.93 Mbits/sec']
mininet-wifi> sta1 iw dev sta1-wlan0 link
Connected to 02:00:00:00:03:00 (on sta1-wlan0)
        SSID: new-ssid
        freq: 5180
        RX: 840551 bytes (12506 packets)
        TX: 23301226 bytes (15251 packets)
        signal: -64 dBm
        tx bitrate: 9.0 MBit/s

        bss flags:         short-slot-time
        dtim period:       2
        beacon int:        100
```

Note that the bitrate was limited to 9 Mbits/s and the measurement from *iperf* dropped to less than 6 Mbits/s.

Finally, let us make another bitrate change and measure the bandwidth once more.

```
mininet-wifi> sta1 iw dev sta1-wlan0 set bitrates legacy-5 6
mininet-wifi> iperf sta1 sta2
*** Iperf: testing TCP bandwidth between sta1 and sta2
*** Results: ['4.37 Mbits/sec', '4.44 Mbits/sec']
mininet-wifi> sta1 iw dev sta1-wlan0 link
Connected to 02:00:00:00:03:00 (on sta1-wlan0)
        SSID: new-ssid
        freq: 5180
        RX: 1044693 bytes (16503 packets)
        TX: 26353234 bytes (17256 packets)
        signal: -64 dBm
        tx bitrate: 6.0 MBit/s

        bss flags:         short-slot-time
        dtim period:       2
        beacon int:        100
```

Once again the available bandwidth dropped and the *bitrate* was limited to 6 Mbits/s, as defined by the command.

Another interesting test is to verify the difference in the transfer rate supported by different Wi-Fi standards. For example, since the script is configured to operate on the IEEE 802.11a standard, which supports up to 54 Mbits/s, it was possible to get the 14 Mbits/s acquired in the previous test. On the other hand, another standard, IEEE 802.11b, would support only up to 11 Mbits/s.

Let us carry out a simple test: change the operating mode of the script from *mode='a'* to *mode='b'*, and change the channel from 36 to 1. Then run *iperf* one more time and observe the result.

 Due to a lack of knowledge, many users end up making mistakes when they configure the channel on an access point. What happens is that, for example, channel one does not work at 5 GHz, the frequency used in the IEEE 802.11a standard. You cannot, thus, use channel strips that are not compatible with certain 802.11 standards. The document available on *hostapd*[9] can serve as a good reference point to identify the correct channels for certain operating standards.

```
mininet-wifi> iperf sta1 sta2
*** Iperf: testing TCP bandwidth between sta1 and sta2
*** Results: ['4.50 Mbits/sec', '4.57 Mbits/sec']
```

As you can see, the measured bandwidth was 4.5 Mbits/s, which is limited to 11 Mbits/s, exactly as defined by the IEEE 802.11b standard.

2.11 Distance *versus* throughput

Throughput is the ability to transmit data from one network point to another over a period of time, determining the speed at which data travels through a link. In wireless networks, throughput is, in theory, highly impacted by the distance between two nodes.

---

[9]https://w1.fi/cgit/hostap/plain/hostapd/hostapd.conf

Among the tools for measuring throughput, *iperf* is certainly the one that stands out the most, as it is the preferred tool in most cases. Throughput measurement using *iperf* is relatively simple, since two nodes executing it are enough for it to function, with one of the nodes operating as client and the other as server.

In order to run *iperf* to verify the relation between distance and bandwidth, we will use the <*position.py*> file as a basis.

```
~/mininet-wifi$ sudo python examples/position.py
```

After running it, you will see a topology with two stations and one access point.

Since the script file has been successfully executed, let us measure the throughput between sta1 and sta2 according to their initial arrangement.

```
mininet-wifi> iperf sta1 sta2
*** Iperf: testing TCP bandwidth between sta1 and sta2
*** Results: ['8.42 Mbits/sec', '9.04 Mbits/sec']
```

Keep a record of the result observed in this test round. *The result may suffer slight variations.*

Now, we will change the positions of sta1 and sta2 so that they are further away from access point ap1. Then we will measure the throughput between sta1 and sta2 again.

```
mininet-wifi> py sta1.setPosition('40,90,0')
mininet-wifi> py sta2.setPosition('60,10,0')
mininet-wifi> iperf sta1 sta2
*** Iperf: testing TCP bandwidth between sta1 and sta2
*** Results: ['6.98 Mbits/sec', '7.14 Mbits/sec']
```

Comparing this new result with the previous one, it is clear that the more distant the stations are from the access point, the smaller the throughput tends to be.

 In Mininet-WiFi, the `iperf sta1 sta2` command automatically defines `sta1` as a server and `sta2` as a client. Later on we will see examples of the most common way of using *iperf*.

Publications that have already used Mininet-WiFi for performance research:
- Gilani S.M.M., Heang H.M., Hong T., Zhao G., Xu C. *OpenFlow-Based Load Balancing in WLAN: Throughput Analysis*. Communications, Signal Processing, and Systems (CSPS), 2016.
- Krishna Vijay Singh, Sakshi Gupta, Saurabh Verma, Mayank Pandey. *Improving performance of TCP for wireless network using SDN*. Proceedings of ICDCN, 2019.

2.12 Mobility models

Mobility models are also very important because they try to mimic the mobility of persons, vehicles or any other object that is mobile, i.e. able to move from one point to another. There are several studies that try to identify the patterns of human mobility during natural disasters, such as major storms, floods, etc.

As for the propagation models, there are several mobility models that are accepted by the scientific community worldwide, and some of them are supported by Mininet-WiFi, such as *Random Direction, Random Walk, Gauss Markov*, among other models. Mobility can be observed either using CLI or a graph, as illustrated in Figure 2.9.

Because of their importance, we will now check how mobility models can be configured on Mininet-WiFi. To do so, let us use the *<mobilityModel.py>* script, which contains the *Random Direction* mobility model in its code. It is important to note that for each mobility model there may be unique parameters such as minimum and maximum speed limits, areas where nodes can move, etc. All the information you need about mobility model settings can be found on Mininet-WiFi's web page[10].

Seed is one of the most important mobility model settings. It modifies mobility significantly. For instance, if a *seed* number one causes the nodes to move from certain x and y values, a seed number two will change the initial values of x and y. It will not be able to change the mobility behavior, but it may

---

[10]http://mininet-wifi.github.io/

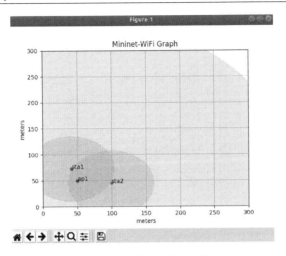

Figure 2.9: Working with mobility.

change its own initial positions. This is an important feature because the initial arrangement of the nodes may not always meet the requirements defined for a particular experiment.

Now that we know a little more about the theory of mobility models, let us run the following script and observe how the nodes behave when configured with the *Random Direction* mobility model.

```
~/mininet-wifi$ sudo python examples/mobilityModel.py
```

 Record the behavior of the nodes and try to change the mobility model at a later time for comparison purposes.

Then we will test two of the three implemented Mininet-WiFi commands that were presented in the 2.2 section: `stop` and `start`.

Let us first try the `stop` command.

```
mininet-wifi> stop
```

Should everything go as expected, the `stop` command will cease mobility, causing the nodes to stop moving. This feature is useful in cases where the user wishes to observe information such as signal strength or even available bandwidth connected to an arrangement of nodes.

Now, we can issue the `start` command to resume mobility.

```
mininet-wifi> start
```

 All mobility models supported by Mininet-WiFi can be found in *<mn_wifi/mobility.py>*. Should you want to implement new mobility models, you must include them in this file.

 Studies that previously used Mininet-WiFi for research on mobility:
- K. V. K. Singh, M. Pandey. *Software-defined mobility in IP based Wi-Fi networks: Design proposal and future directions*. IEEE ANTS, 2016
- D. Tu, Z. Zhao and H. Zhang. *ISD-WiFi: An intelligent SDN based solution for enterprise WLANs*. WCSP, 2016,
- A. Kaul, L. Xue, K. Obraczka, M. Santos, T. Turletti. WiMobtitHandover and Load Balancing for Distributed Network Control: Applications in ITS Message Dissemination. ICCCN, 2018.
- Z. Han, T. Lei, Z. Lu, X. Wen, W. Zheng, L. Guo. *Artificial Intelligence Based Handoff Management for Dense WLANs: A Deep Reinforcement Learning Approach*. IEEE Access, 2019.

Level: intermediate

3. Intermediate

In this chapter we will explore tutorials and concepts related to computer networks as a whole, but focusing on wireless networks, of course. The Open-Flow protocol will also be introduced, and some peculiarities regarding its use in wireless networks shall be discussed.

To do the next tutorials, consider creating a repository clone of mn-wifi-book-en, which is available at https://github.com/ramonfontes/mn-wifi-book-en. All scripts we will use to complete the tutorials will be available in this repository.

```
~/mininet-wifi$ git clone https://github.com/ramonfontes/mn-wifi-book-en
```

3.1 Network interfaces

In this section, we will learn to manipulate network interfaces by defining multiple interfaces for stations. We will also learn how to apply the concept of binding and bonding interfaces.

3.1.1 Setting multiple interfaces

By default, a station has only one wireless network interface. However, there may be cases that require the use of multiple interfaces per station. These cases may be related to the creation of backup interfaces, or even to actions aimed at aggregating and increasing bandwidth, among other possibilities.

Since multiple interfaces is a very relevant topic and is often not known by many users, we will learn how to add them, and explore some scenarios where they can be applied. Let us start at the code level by considering the example below, where a call is made to *net.addStation()*, which is the method responsible for creating stations in Mininet-WiFi.

```
sta1 = net.addStation('sta1', wlans=2)
```

By setting up *wlans=2*, two wireless interfaces for sta1 should be created: sta1-wlan0 and sta1-wlan1. Let us use *<multipleWlan.py>* as an example, which includes definition for *wlans*.

```
~/mininet-wifi$ sudo python mn-wifi-book-en/codes/cap3/multipleWlan.py
```

After running it, you will be able to notice the presence of the aforementioned interfaces, as can be seen below.

```
mininet-wifi> sta1 ip add show
1: lo: <LOOPBACK,UP,LOWER_UP> mtu 65536 qdisc noqueue state UNKNOWN group
↪ default qlen 1000
    link/loopback 00:00:00:00:00:00 brd 00:00:00:00:00:00
    inet 127.0.0.1/8 scope host lo
        valid_lft forever preferred_lft forever
    inet6 ::1/128 scope host
        valid_lft forever preferred_lft forever
1030: sta1-wlan0: <BROADCAST,MULTICAST,UP,LOWER_UP> mtu 1500 qdisc htb state UP
↪ group default qlen 1000
    link/ether 02:00:00:00:00:00 brd ff:ff:ff:ff:ff:ff
    inet 10.0.0.1/8 scope global sta1-wlan0
        valid_lft forever preferred_lft forever
    inet6 fe80::ff:fe00:0/64 scope link
        valid_lft forever preferred_lft forever
1031: sta1-wlan1: <NO-CARRIER,BROADCAST,MULTICAST,UP> mtu 1500 qdisc mq state
↪ DOWN group default qlen 1000
    link/ether 02:00:00:00:01:00 brd ff:ff:ff:ff:ff:ff
    inet 192.168.10.1/24 scope global sta1-wlan1
        valid_lft forever preferred_lft forever
```

These interfaces can be linked to work together in order to increase the capacity of transferring and receiving data. They can also be associated with
different access points and maintain connectivity when there is a problem with
one of the access points, for instance.

To illustrate this, we can verify through *iwconfig* that both sta1-wlan0 and
sta1-wlan1 are associated with different access points. While the first interface is associated with an access point, the second one is part of an *ad hoc*
network, which is identified by the *adhoc1* SSID.

```
mininet-wifi> sta1 iwconfig
lo        no wireless extensions.

sta1-wlan1  IEEE 802.11  ESSID:"adhoc1"
          Mode:Ad-Hoc  Frequency:2.412 GHz  Cell: 02:CA:FF:EE:BA:01
          Tx-Power=14 dBm
          Retry short limit:7   RTS thr:off   Fragment thr:off
          Encryption key:off
          Power Management:off

sta1-wlan0  IEEE 802.11  ESSID:"ssid_1"
          Mode:Managed  Frequency:2.432 GHz  Access Point:
          ↪  02:00:00:00:03:00
          Bit Rate:54 Mb/s   Tx-Power=14 dBm
          Retry short limit:7   RTS thr:off   Fragment thr:off
          Encryption key:off
          Power Management:off
          Link Quality=70/70  Signal level=-36 dBm
          Rx invalid nwid:0  Rx invalid crypt:0  Rx invalid frag:0
          Tx excessive retries:0  Invalid misc:9   Missed beacon:0
```

After this brief introduction on how to define multiple interfaces for different
nodes in Mininet-WiFi, we will now learn a little more about the benefits that
can be achieved with the use of multiple network interfaces, especially over
bonding interfaces. But first, let us also have an introduction to the process
of binding interfaces, by assigning multiple IP addresses to a single network
interface.

3.1.2 Binding interfaces

 Requirement(s): script(s) only

Binding is the term used when multiple IP addresses are assigned to the same interface of a given node. It is a type of solution widely used when trying to make a node respond to different IP addresses. For example, the simplest topology of Mininet-WiFi creates a node called sta1 that has only one wireless network interface (sta1-wlan0), which has the default IP address 10.0.0.1/8. For an additional IP address to be assigned to that interface, the following command could be used:

```
~/mininet-wifi$ sudo mn --wifi
mininet-wifi> sta1 ip addr add 192.168.1.1/24 dev sta1-wlan0 label
↪  sta1-wlan0:0
```

In fact, this command will create a virtual interface (or sub-interface) called sta1-wlan0:0, and it will also set the new IP address for this interface, as follows:

```
mininet-wifi> sta1 ip addr show sta1-wlan0
9: sta1-wlan0: <NO-CARRIER,BROADCAST,MULTICAST,UP,LOWER_UP> mtu 1500 qdisc
↪  htb state DORMANT group default qlen 1000
   link/ether 02:00:00:00:00:00 brd ff:ff:ff:ff:ff:ff
   inet 10.0.0.1/8 scope global sta1-wlan0
      valid_lft forever preferred_lft forever
   inet 192.168.1.1/24 scope global sta1-wlan0:0
      valid_lft forever preferred_lft forever
```

Thus, if the 192.168.1.2/24 IP is assigned to sta2, both sta1 and sta2 will be able to respond to two IP addresses, as follows.

```
mininet-wifi> sta2 ip addr add 192.168.1.2/24 dev sta2-wlan0 label
↪  sta2-wlan0:0

mininet-wifi> sta1 ping -c1 192.168.1.2
PING 192.168.1.2 (192.168.1.2) 56(84) bytes of data.
64 bytes from 192.168.1.2: icmp_seq=1 ttl=64 time=0.070 ms

--- 192.168.1.2 ping statistics ---
1 packets transmitted, 1 received, 0% packet loss, time 0ms
rtt min/avg/max/mdev = 0.070/0.070/0.070/0.000 ms

mininet-wifi> sta1 ping -c1 10.0.0.2
```

```
PING 10.0.0.2 (10.0.0.2) 56(84) bytes of data.
64 bytes from 10.0.0.2: icmp_seq=1 ttl=64 time=0.110 ms

--- 10.0.0.2 ping statistics ---
1 packets transmitted, 1 received, 0% packet loss, time 0ms
rtt min/avg/max/mdev = 0.110/0.110/0.110/0.000 ms
```

Binding can be very useful when you do not have access to many resources or
enough network interfaces.

3.1.3 Bonding interfaces

 Requirement(s): *Ryu*

Bonding interfaces, in turn, consist of a process of combining or merging two
or more network interfaces into a single interface for the purpose of offering
performance improvements and even redundancy. For instance, you could
increase network throughput, or make it so that if one bonding interface is inac-
tive or disconnected, another one could supply the demand and act as a backup.

In Linux systems, a special kernel module called bonding is used to connect multiple network interfaces into a single interface. In other words, two or
more network interfaces can be connected through a single logical interface.
Naturally, the behavior of bonding interfaces depends on the mode of operation being used. In this tutorial we will cover two of the supported methods
(or modes) indicated in the documentation available at the official web page
for bonding[1]: link aggregation and broadcast modes.

Identified by the number four, the first mode of operation to be addressed is
link (or interface) aggregation (IEEE 802.3ad). *We recommend that you read
<bonding.py> for details on how to configure this bonding interface mode.*
Link or interface aggregation can be done in basically two ways: static, where
each device is directly instructed; or dynamically, through the use of a protocol
called Link Aggregation Control Protocol (LACP). In this tutorial we will use
the dynamic method, and the necessary rules for operation will be applied by
running *Ryu* with a module called *simple_switch_lacp_13*, which has enough

---

[1]https://wiki.linuxfoundation.org/networking/bonding

instructions for link aggregation with the LACP protocol.

To start *Ryu* with the module that supports the LACP protocol, you will need to issue the following command.

```
~/mininet-wifi/ryu/$ ryu-manager ryu/app/simple_switch_lacp_13.py
```

Then, run *<bonding.py>* in a new terminal.

```
~/mininet-wifi$ sudo python mn-wifi-book-en/codes/cap3/bonding.py
```

The *<bonding.py>* file consists of three hosts connected to a switch. Host h1 has two interfaces that will work in aggregate way. Both are connected to the s1 switch, as shown in Figure 3.1.

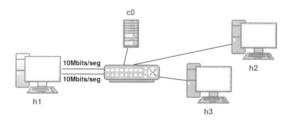

Figure 3.1: *Bonding* interface.

You will now need to open four terminals by starting *xterm* from the Mininet-WiFi CLI. Note that two terminals are required for host h1.

```
mininet-wifi> xterm h1 h1 h2 h3
```

On h1's terminals, run *iperf* as follows.

```
h1-t2# iperf -s -i 1 -p 6700
-----------------------------------------------------------
Server listening on TCP port 6700
TCP window size: 85.3 KByte (default)
-----------------------------------------------------------

h1-t1# iperf -s -i 1 -p 6701
-----------------------------------------------------------
Server listening on TCP port 6701
TCP window size: 85.3 KByte (default)
-----------------------------------------------------------
```

At this point, h1 is waiting for connections that must be requested by clients, which will be the h2 and h3 nodes in this case. Commands must be run simultaneously, in the shortest possible time interval for better comprehension.

```
h2# iperf -c 10.0.0.1 -i 1 -p 6700

h3# iperf -c 10.0.0.1 -i 1 -p 6701
```

Should all occur as expected, you will be possible to note, on the terminals pertaining to h1, the connection requests sent by h2 and h3, which result in a similar output, as shown next.

```
h1-t1#
[ 17]  0.0- 1.0 sec  1.14 MBytes  9.60 Mbits/sec
[ 17]  1.0- 2.0 sec  1.14 MBytes  9.57 Mbits/sec
[ 17]  2.0- 3.0 sec  1.14 MBytes  9.56 Mbits/sec
[ 17]  3.0- 4.0 sec  1.14 MBytes  9.57 Mbits/sec
[ 17]  4.0- 5.0 sec  1.14 MBytes  9.57 Mbits/sec
[ 17]  5.0- 6.0 sec  1.14 MBytes  9.56 Mbits/sec
[ 17]  6.0- 7.0 sec  1.14 MBytes  9.57 Mbits/sec
[ 17]  7.0- 8.0 sec  1.14 MBytes  9.57 Mbits/sec
[ 17]  8.0- 9.0 sec  1.14 MBytes  9.56 Mbits/sec
[ 17]  9.0-10.0 sec  1.14 MBytes  9.57 Mbits/sec

h1-t2#
[ 17]  1.0- 2.0 sec  1.14 MBytes  9.57 Mbits/sec
[ 17]  2.0- 3.0 sec  1.14 MBytes  9.56 Mbits/sec
[ 17]  3.0- 4.0 sec  1.14 MBytes  9.57 Mbits/sec
[ 17]  4.0- 5.0 sec  1.14 MBytes  9.57 Mbits/sec
[ 17]  5.0- 6.0 sec  1.14 MBytes  9.56 Mbits/sec
[ 17]  6.0- 7.0 sec  1.14 MBytes  9.57 Mbits/sec
[ 17]  7.0- 8.0 sec  1.14 MBytes  9.57 Mbits/sec
[ 17]  8.0- 9.0 sec  1.14 MBytes  9.56 Mbits/sec
[ 17]  9.0-10.0 sec  1.14 MBytes  9.57 Mbits/sec
```

Since the bandwidth between h1 and s1 is limited to 10 Mbit/s, link aggregation enables h1 to respond to the two simultaneous requests by h2 and h3, preserving the full bandwidth of each connection to s1. Without link aggregation, h1 would only be able to account for half the bandwidth, something around 4.5 Mbits/s for each node (h2 and h3).

Finally, we will check the amount of packets sent and received by h1. *The loopback interface was omitted from the output.*

```
mininet-wifi> h1 ifconfig
bond0: flags=5187<UP,BROADCAST,RUNNING,MASTER,MULTICAST>  mtu 1500
    inet 10.0.0.1  netmask 255.0.0.0  broadcast 0.0.0.0
    inet6 fe80::200:ff:fe11:2233  prefixlen 64  scopeid 0x20<link>
    ether 00:00:00:11:22:33  txqueuelen 1000  (Ethernet)
    RX packets 9662  bytes 27669062 (26.3 MiB)
    RX errors 0  dropped 0  overruns 0  frame 0
    TX packets 9188  bytes 607324 (593.0 KiB)
    TX errors 0  dropped 0 overruns 0  carrier 0  collisions 0

h1-eth0: flags=6211<UP,BROADCAST,RUNNING,SLAVE,MULTICAST>  mtu 1500
    ether 00:00:00:11:22:33  txqueuelen 1000  (Ethernet)
    RX packets 4833  bytes 13834677 (13.1 MiB)
    RX errors 0  dropped 0  overruns 0  frame 0
    TX packets 4600  bytes 304136 (297.0 KiB)
    TX errors 0  dropped 0 overruns 0  carrier 0  collisions 0

h1-eth1: flags=6211<UP,BROADCAST,RUNNING,SLAVE,MULTICAST>  mtu 1500
    ether 00:00:00:11:22:33  txqueuelen 1000  (Ethernet)
    RX packets 4832  bytes 13834651 (13.1 MiB)
    RX errors 0  dropped 0  overruns 0  frame 0
    TX packets 4590  bytes 303368 (296.2 KiB)
    TX errors 0  dropped 0 overruns 0  carrier 0  collisions 0
```

 The ifconfig command was used to display a more organized output in comparison to *ip -s link*.

If we compare the amount of data sent to the amount of data received by h1, we can see that there is a certain balance between h1-eth0 and h1-eth1. This would be the expected result, since both were able to respond to the same requests sent by h2 and h3.

 The *simple_switch_lacp_13* module supported by *Ryu* is funda-mental for link aggregation to function as expected. However, it is not the only module available, and you will certainly find similar ones for the various SDN controllers.

 Try to run *sh ovs-ofctl dump-flows s1* on the Mininet-WiFi CLI to observe the flows created by the SDN controller.

Now, let us put into practice a scenario a little different from the one using link aggregation, which employs, instead, the broadcast mode. This mode provides fault tolerance in cases of interface failure. For example, when one interface becomes unavailable, another one can respond to requests and keep the service active.

Let us learn how to use it by practical means. First, you need to start the same code as before, but using the -b parameter this time, as shown below. Since *Ryu* is not required for this new tutorial, its process should be killed.

```
~/mininet-wifi$ sudo python mn-wifi-book-en/codes/cap3/bonding.py -b
```

Then, let us try a *ping* between h2 and h1.

```
mininet-wifi> h2 ping -c5 10.0.0.1
PING 10.0.0.1 (10.0.0.1) 56(84) bytes of data.
64 bytes from 10.0.0.1: icmp_seq=1 ttl=64 time=36.9 ms
64 bytes from 10.0.0.1: icmp_seq=1 ttl=64 time=39.4 ms (DUP!)
64 bytes from 10.0.0.1: icmp_seq=2 ttl=64 time=0.224 ms
64 bytes from 10.0.0.1: icmp_seq=2 ttl=64 time=0.258 ms (DUP!)
```

 Why is every ICMP packet sent answered with another ending with the *DUP!* message? Because for each ICMP *request*, h1 responds with two ICMP reply packets, one for each interface connected to the s1 switch. Then, for each received packet (whether it be ICMP or any other type), h1's interfaces will respond to duplicate packets in order to provide fault tolerance.

To understand a little more about how this fault tolerance works, let us disable the h1-eth0 interface to simulate a fault while h2 communicates with h1. To do so, we will open a terminal for h1 from the Mininet-WiFi CLI to do a ping attempt from h2 to h1.

```
mininet-wifi> xterm h1
```

```
mininet-wifi> h2 ping -c5 10.0.0.1
PING 10.0.0.1 (10.0.0.1) 56(84) bytes of data.
64 bytes from 10.0.0.1: icmp_seq=1 ttl=64 time=0.529 ms
64 bytes from 10.0.0.1: icmp_seq=1 ttl=64 time=0.559 ms (DUP!)
64 bytes from 10.0.0.1: icmp_seq=2 ttl=64 time=0.149 ms
```

```
64 bytes from 10.0.0.1: icmp_seq=2 ttl=64 time=0.151 ms (DUP!)
64 bytes from 10.0.0.1: icmp_seq=3 ttl=64 time=0.193 ms
64 bytes from 10.0.0.1: icmp_seq=4 ttl=64 time=0.112 ms
64 bytes from 10.0.0.1: icmp_seq=5 ttl=64 time=0.115 ms

--- 10.0.0.1 ping statistics ---
5 packets transmitted, 5 received, +2 duplicates, 0% packet loss, time
↪ 4085ms
rtt min/avg/max/mdev = 0.112/0.258/0.559/0.182 ms
```

While the *ping* command is in progress, disable the h1-eth0 interface created by h1.

```
h1# ip link set h1-eth0 down
```

As in the previous case, you can see that some ICMP packets were duplicated (as with the first two packets), since the h1-eth0 interface was still active. However, after deactivating it, h1 was able to respond to h2 by using its unique active interface. In other words, the service remained uninterrupted even when one of the interfaces became unavailable.

3.2   Traffic analysis

3.2.1   Capturing packets

 Requirement(s): *Wireshark*

Now let us learn how to capture packets and then how to capture beacons. If you are already familiar with computer networks, you have certainly used the *ping* tool before and not just in the tutorials described in this book. Nonetheless, few have the curiosity to analyze in greater detail how the communication between two nodes occurs.

In this tutorial we will generate traffic using the *ping* tool and capture it with *Wireshark*, one of the most widely used programs in the world for network traffic analysis. The goal here is to learn how network traffic analysis can be performed and, more importantly, to understand how *ping* works in practice. To do so, let us start Mininet-WiFi's simplest topology.

```
~/mininet-wifi$ sudo mn --wifi
```

Then we run *Wireshark* from sta1:

```
mininet-wifi> sta1 wireshark &
```

With *Wireshark* open, look for the interface named sta1-wlan0 and then begin capturing in this interface.

Now, in the Mininet-WiFi CLI, try carrying out a *ping* to sta2 from sta1. The output of the *ping* command usually consists of the size of the packet (in bytes), the name of the target machine, the ICMP packet sequence number (icmp_seq), TTL and latency (in milliseconds (ms)).

```
mininet-wifi> sta1 ping -c1 sta2
PING 10.0.0.2 (10.0.0.2) 56(84) bytes of data.
64 bytes from 10.0.0.2: icmp_seq=1 ttl=64 time=0.100 ms

--- 10.0.0.2 ping statistics ---
1 packets transmitted, 1 received, 0% packet loss, time 0ms
rtt min/avg/max/mdev = 0.100/0.100/0.100/0.000 ms
```

After running *ping*, you will be able to notice in *Wireshark* the presence of the ARP and ICMP protocols, as shown in Figure 3.2. The ARP protocol is a layer 2 protocol of the OSI reference model and is responsible for the resolution of MAC addresses. Once the MAC address portion has been resolved, the ICMP packets appear.

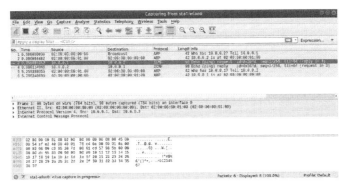

Figure 3.2: Packets captured by sta1.

By doing this simple test you can see, via *Wireshark*, that there are only two messages belonging to the ICMP protocol: *request* and *reply*. The first one refers to the *ping* request, which originates from sta1 (10.0.0.1), while the second one refers to the response, whose origin is sta2 and destination is sta1.

Besides *Wireshark*, another widely used tool for analyzing network traffic is *tcpdump*[2]. Working with *tcpdump* is relatively simple, but before using it you will need to close the previously opened instance of Mininet-WiFi, run it again, and then open a separate terminal for sta1, as follows.

```
mininet-wifi> exit
~/mininet-wifi$ sudo mn --wifi
mininet-wifi> xterm sta1
```

On the sta1 terminal run *tcpdump* as shown below. The *-i* parameter instructs *tcpdump* as to which interface will be used for traffic capture.

```
sta1# tcpdump -i sta1-wlan0
```

Then, using the Mininet-WiFi CLI, *ping* between sta1 and sta2.

```
mininet-wifi> sta1 ping -c1 sta2
PING 10.0.0.2 (10.0.0.2) 56(84) bytes of data.
64 bytes from 10.0.0.2: icmp_seq=1 ttl=64 time=0.121 ms

--- 10.0.0.2 ping statistics ---
1 packets transmitted, 1 received, 0% packet loss, time 0ms
rtt min/avg/max/mdev = 0.121/0.121/0.121/0.000 ms
```

Now, look at the sta1 terminal to observe the packets. Note that the output displayed there is quite similar to the information obtained by *Wireshark*.

```
10:14:20.025022 ARP, Request who-has 10.0.0.2 tell alpha-Inspiron, length
↪  28
10:14:20.025100 ARP, Reply 10.0.0.2 is-at 02:00:00:00:01:00 (oui Unknown),
↪  length 28
10:14:20.025104 IP alpha-Inspiron > 10.0.0.2: ICMP echo request, id 13535,
↪  seq 1, length 64
10:14:20.025126 IP 10.0.0.2 > alpha-Inspiron: ICMP echo reply, id 13535,
↪  seq 1, length 64
```

---

[2]tcpdump.org/

Why was it necessary to shut down Mininet-WiFi and run it again? Because an ARP table was created in sta1 in the previous *ping* attempt. Restarting the process from scratch forces the creation of a new ARP table. Try running the "sta1 arp -a" command from the Mininet-WiFi CLI to check the ARP table created in sta1.

Tcpdump allows capture files to be saved in the pcap format for later analysis, or for porting to other systems for analysis as well. That is, you can also use *tcpdump* to generate files that can be read by *Wireshark*.

For example, the command below will create a file called *<mycap-file.pcapng>*.

```
sta1# tcpdump -i sta1-wlan0 -w mycap-file.pcapng
```

Further information about *tcpdump* can found on its official website or by running the tcpdump --help command.

3.2.2 Capturing beacons

 Requirement(s): *Wireshark*

Beacons are wireless management frames (WLANs) based on WiFi (IEEE 802.11). They contain all the information about the wireless network, such as SSID, signal level, among other factors. When using Infrastructure mode (or Basic Infrastructure Services Set (BSS)), beacons serve to advertise the presence of a wireless LAN and to synchronize the members of the service set. In networks that do not have an access point (IBSS), the task of signal generation is distributed among stations.

In this tutorial we will learn to capture beacons in a BSS network. To do so, let us run the simplest Mininet-WiFi topology.

```
~/mininet-wifi$ sudo mn --wifi
```

Since beacon capture cannot be done by interfaces operating in managed mode, you will need to create a monitor interface. Monitor interfaces allow

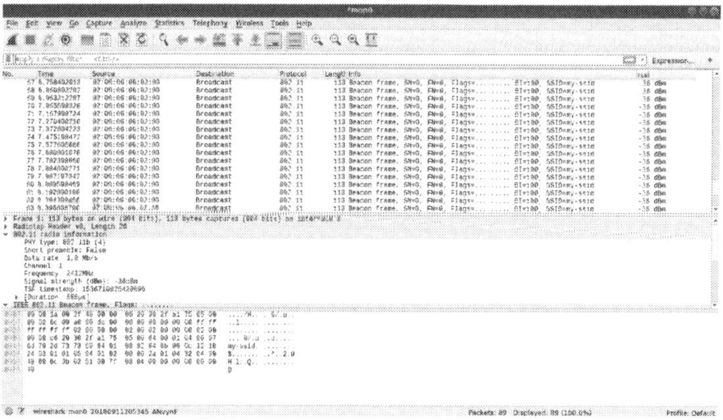

[Figure: Wireshark capture window screenshot]

Figure 3.3: Captured beacons by sta1.

the capture of beacons from all access points within reach of a client, even if the interfaces are not associated with the access point.

To create a *monitor* interface, use the following command.

```
mininet-wifi> sta1 iw dev sta1-wlan0 interface add mon0 type monitor
mininet-wifi> sta1 ip link set mon0 up
```

Then run *Wireshark*:

```
mininet-wifi> sta1 wireshark &
```

In *Wireshark*, search for the *mon0* monitor interface, and start the capturing processes from this interface. Then it should be possible to see the beacons captured by sta1 on the *mon0* interface, which are sent by access point ap1, as shown in Figure 3.3. Remember that in a *BSS* network beacons are sent by the access points that constitute the network.

 Try doing the same with mesh or *ad hoc*. Both *<mesh.py>* and *<adhoc.py>*, which are available in the *</examples>* directory, may be useful in this task.

3.2.3 Spectrum analysis

 Requirement(s): *linssid*

Wireless communication signals tend to behave in unpredictable ways. You have probably seen how quickly the signal indicator on your smartphone or laptop oscillates between full and empty. A few steps in the wrong direction are enough to substantially weaken the signal, and if you are like many people who work with IT, you probably carry a mental map of your home WiFi network to avoid weak signals. Maybe you have even moved a piece of furniture in your room so you could enjoy higher and better download and upload rates.

Signals from wireless devices such as WiFi routers are influenced by interference, obstructions and various other factors that may affect the performance of the router. Even if the router is configured to operate at a certain frequency, we cannot expect the signal range to be the same in all directions. Moreover, it may be operating at the same frequency as nearby routers, and this presents a problem: how would you be able to identify the most appropriate frequency for a particular situation, let alone the best location to install a wireless router, if the signal distribution is not the same? The answer is quite simple: by using wireless spectrum analysis tools such as *linssid*.

That is exactly what we are going to do now. Let us use the *linssid* spectrum analyzer to identify the best or most suitable configuration for a particular topology. If *linssid* is not installed, do so using the following command:

```
~/mininet-wifi$ sudo apt install linssid
```

Then run *<wmediumd_2aps.py>*.

```
~/mininet-wifi$ sudo python mn-wifi-book-en/codes/cap3/wmediumd_2aps.py
```

And open *linssid* from sta1.

```
mininet-wifi> sta1 linssid &
```

In *linssid* search for the option to start captures and check the result while the analysis is performed. At the same time, change sta1's position to the following coordinates.

```
mininet-wifi> py sta1.setPosition('20,20,0')
```

At some point you will be able to notice a new wireless signal originating from access point ap2, as shown in Figure 3.4.

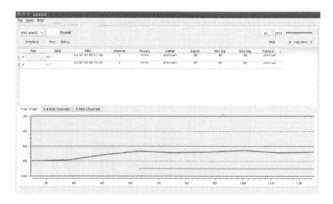

Figure 3.4: *linssid* capture screen with two access points.

After this brief introduction to *linssid*, let us understand how a spectrum analyzer can help in the proper configuration of an access point.

If Mininet-WiFi is running, close it and then run <*wmediumd_3aps.py*>. The topology of this script consists of three access points arranged according to Figure 3.5. Note the channels on which each access point is operating.

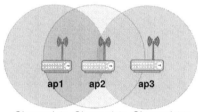

Channel 1:   Channel 6:   Channel 11:
2.412Mhz   2.437Mhz   2.462Mhz

Figure 3.5: Signal overlapping among three access points.

```
mininet-wifi> exit
~/mininet-wifi$ sudo python mn-wifi-book-en/codes/cap3/wmediumd_3aps.py
```

And then run *linssid* from sta1 again.

```
mininet-wifi> sta1 linssid &
```

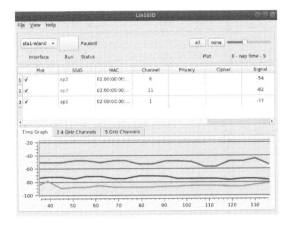

Figure 3.6: *linssid* capture screen with three access points.

After initiating capture with *linssid*, you can see the signals captured by sta1. You can notice, on *linssid*, that access points ap1, ap2 and ap3 are operating on channels 1, 6 and 11, respectively, as shown in Figure 3.6. This would be the most recommended configuration for such topology, since the most basic rule of a WiFi project says that you should not use the same channels, or those near each other with a distance of less than five units, with access points that are geographically close to each other.

Three access points - channels 1, 6 and 11 - are those that do not overlap at 2.4 GHz. What would happen if the topology had more than three access points? In this case, it would be necessary to reuse channels, and some level of interference could occur.

 Every channel operates at a certain frequency. For example: channel 1 operates at 2.412 MHz, channel 6 at 2.437 MHz and channel 11 at 2.462 MHz. The difference in MHz for each channel is 5 MHz, which means that channel 2 operates at 2.417 MHz and so on.

3.2.4   Network telemetry

 Requirement(s): *script(s) only*

Continuous monitoring is an essential part of monitoring networks with a
high level of detail in order to correctly identify and characterize situations
related to equipment failure and performance, as well as to detect security
issues and to perform traffic engineering. As networks constantly grow in size,
complexity and traffic volume, the need for continuous and precise monitoring is greater than ever before. We can summarize network telemetry as an
understanding of what is happening on a given network.

Network telemetry is emerging as a powerful way to support these needs.
With the trend of Software-Defined Networking, network management solutions have become more automated than before. At its highest level, it is a
push-based approach to monitoring: data plane devices such as switches and
routers stream data about traffic and performance to the software that performs
analytics.

In this simple tutorial, we will learn how to enable a simple telemetry implementation. It is important to stress, however, that the solution shown below
was designed to make life easier for users who experience some difficulty in
programming. Other telemetry tools can not only effortlessly support other
types of data not compatible with Mininet-WiFi, but also be easily used with
the latter. One example of this is *sFlow*, which will be introduced in 4.2.

For this tutorial, consider running <*telemetry.py*>. The topology represented
in this script consists of three stations exclusively associated with a single AP.

```
~/mininet-wifi$ sudo python mn-wifi-book-en/codes/cap3/telemetry.py
```

After running the script a figure similar to Figure 3.7 will appear, which shows
the stations' RSSI while the code is running. Observing it, we can draw a
conclusion: sta1 is experiencing better signal strength compared to the other
stations.

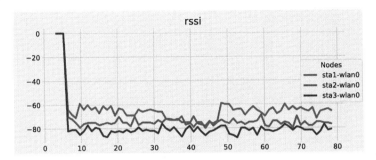

Figure 3.7: Network telemetry.

After while, you can change `sta1`'s position. The position shown below will move the station away from the AP, causing the signal to oscillate downward.

```
mininet-wifi> py sta1.setPosition('10,10,0')
```

Then, after moving the station closer to the AP, the received signal improves significantly.

```
mininet-wifi> py sta1.setPosition('10,40,0')
```

In addition to RSSIs, other data types are also automatically supported, such as those located in the statistics directory[3], as well as position and other information. You only need to change the data_type variable in the *<telemetry.py>* file to get the information you wish. It is worth mentioning that all traces are saved in a file that can be used later for more detailed analyses.

   Mininet-WiFi: Telemetry:
    `https://youtu.be/5cF9Ge_iozw`

---

[3]/sys/class/ieee80211/{ }/device/net/{ }/statistics/

3.3 Scanning methods

There are basically two scanning methods that a client may use to determine to which access point a station should associate: passive and active scanning.

3.3.1 Active scanning

In active scanning the client transmits a probe request and listens to the probe response from an access point. The probe request usually includes a specific SSID and only access points with a specific SSID will respond.

3.3.2 Passive scanning

In passive scanning the client listens to each channel for beacons periodically sent by access points. Compared to active scanning, passive scanning usually takes longer to achieve results, since the client must listen and wait for beacons and then manually find an access point. Another feature of this type of scanning is that if the client does not wait long enough on a channel, it may lose beacons sent by access points.

 By default, access points regularly broadcast beacons at every 100 ms. Therefore, due to the need to wait for these periodic beacons, clients typically prefer to use the active scanning.

During channel scanning the client is unable to transmit or even receive data. To minimize the consequences of downtime, one approach that can be used is background scanning. In this type of scanning, clients scan the wireless medium before moving to a new access point, which makes the transition between access points faster.

Background scanning

Background scanning (bgscan) is a type of scan performed through *wpa_supplicant* that is done automatically, regardless of whether or not the station is associated with an access point. Once configured, *bgscan* will search, at regular and pre-configured time intervals, for an access point with the best signal in relation to the access point with which the client is currently associated. If an access point with an optimal signal is found, *bgscan* will initiate an association process between the client and the access point.

For *bgscan* to work, all access points must have the same SSID. Both the signal level and the time interval can be customized to aid in its functioning: for example, if -60 dBm is set, *bgscan* will only associate with an access point with a signal level higher than -60 dBm. As to the time, there are two types of timing: *short interval* and *long interval*. The short interval is only used until an access point with a signal strength higher than -60 dBm, for instance, is encountered. After this, the long interval replaces the short interval.

For example, let us use *<bgscan.py>* as a reference point. In it, the signal strength was set to -60 dBm, the short interval to five seconds, and the long interval to ten seconds. Therefore, a scan will be performed every five seconds until an access point with a signal strength higher than -60 dBm is found. If it manages to find the desired access point, scanning will occur every ten seconds.

Bgscan
Given its relevance, let us then check how bgscan works. First, let us run the following script.

```
~/mininet-wifi$ sudo python mn-wifi-book-en/codes/cap3/bgscan.py
```

And then open a terminal for sta1.

```
mininet-wifi> xterm sta1
```

On the sta1 terminal, run *wpa_cli* on sta1-wlan0. *Wpa_cli* is a program used to interact with *wpa_supplicant*. It is also worth mentioning that WPAWPA2 support is provided by *wpa_supplicant* as well.

```
sta1-terminal# wpa_cli -i sta1-wlan0
```

Now, you can notice, on the sta1 terminal, some scans being performed at regular five second intervals, as follows:

```
<3>CTRL-EVENT-SCAN-STARTED
<3>CTRL-EVENT-SCAN-RESULTS     <3>CTRL-EVENT-SCAN-STARTED
<3>CTRL-EVENT-SCAN-RESULTS
```

Note that the scanning process was not able to find access points with better-received signal strength. If we look at sta1's association data, we can see that it is associated with access point ap1 and is broadcasting beacons at -52 dBm.

```
mininet-wifi> sta1 iw dev sta1-wlan0 link
Connected to 00:00:00:00:00:01 (on sta1-wlan0)
    SSID: handover
    freq: 2412
    RX: 2548 bytes (37 packets)
    TX: 742 bytes (7 packets)
    signal: -52 dBm
    tx bitrate: 6.0 MBit/s

    bss flags:       short-slot-time
    dtim period:     2
    beacon int:      100
```

Now, we will change sta1's position using the Mininet-WiFi CLI.

```
mininet-wifi> py sta1.setPosition('100,0,0')
```

Then, returning to the sta1 terminal, you can observe that at some point sta1 will find access point ap2, considering it the "best" access point for a some time.

```
<3>SME: Trying to authenticate with 00:00:00:00:00:02 (SSID='handover'
↪ freq=2437 MHz)
<3>Trying to associate with 00:00:00:00:00:02 (SSID='handover' freq=2437
↪ MHz)
<3>Associated with 00:00:00:00:00:02
<3>CTRL-EVENT-SUBNET-STATUS-UPDATE status=0
<3>WPA: Key negotiation completed with 00:00:00:00:00:02 [PTK=CCMP
↪ GTK=CCMP]
<3>CTRL-EVENT-CONNECTED - Connection to 00:00:00:00:00:02 completed [id=0
↪ id_str=]
<3>CTRL-EVENT-SIGNAL-CHANGE above=0 signal=-75 noise=-92 txrate=24000
```

Finally, after verifying sta1's association status, you should be able to see that in fact there was a change in the association of one access point to another.

```
mininet-wifi> sta1 iw dev sta1-wlan0 link
Connected to 00:00:00:00:00:02 (on sta1-wlan0)
        SSID: handover
        freq: 2437
        RX: 7576 bytes (134 packets)
        TX: 860 bytes (15 packets)
```

```
signal: -75 dBm
tx bitrate: 18.0 MBit/s

bss flags:        short-slot-time
dtim period:      2
beacon int:       100
```

Returning to the sta1 terminal, you can observe that the scanning process continues, but without the possibility of finding any other access point with a better signal strength than the one received from the ap2 access point.

3.4 Wireless mesh and *ad hoc*

 Requirement(s): script(s) only

So far only infrastructure networks have been explored. In this type of network, data transfer always takes place between a station and an access point. As we have seen previously, access points are responsible for capturing and re-transmitting the messages sent by stations. In this case, data transfer never occurs directly between two stations.

Figure 3.8: *Ad hoc* and mesh topology.

Now, in this tutorial we will explore two other types of wireless networks: the wireless *ad hoc* network and wireless mesh network. In both cases we will use the topology shown in Figure 3.8. In this topology there is signal overlap between sta1 and sta2, and between sta2 and sta3.

First, let us learn how wireless mesh networks work. To do so, run <*mesh.py*>.

```
~/mininet-wifi$ sudo python mn-wifi-book-en/codes/cap3/mesh.py
```

Then try to *ping* between sta1 and sta2, and then between sta1 and sta3, as follows.

```
mininet-wifi> sta1 ping -c1 sta2
PING 10.0.0.2 (10.0.0.2) 56(84) bytes of data.
64 bytes from 10.0.0.2: icmp_seq=1 ttl=64 time=4.90 ms

--- 10.0.0.2 ping statistics ---
1 packets transmitted, 1 received, 0% packet loss, time 0ms
rtt min/avg/max/mdev = 4.905/4.905/4.905/0.000 ms
mininet-wifi> sta1 ping -c1 sta3
PING 10.0.0.3 (10.0.0.3) 56(84) bytes of data.
64 bytes from 10.0.0.3: icmp_seq=1 ttl=64 time=6.16 ms

--- 10.0.0.3 ping statistics ---
1 packets transmitted, 1 received, 0% packet loss, time 0ms
rtt min/avg/max/mdev = 6.160/6.160/6.160/0.000 ms
```

As you can see, sta1 is able to communicate with sta2 and sta3, since sta2 is located between sta1 and sta3, enabling sta1 to also communicate with sta3 by means of sta2.

Technically, we can see that the sta2 node is actually located between sta1 and sta3 using the following command.

```
mininet-wifi> sta1 iw dev sta1-mp0 mpath dump
DEST ADDR          NEXT HOP          IFACE     SN METRIC QLEN EXPTIME   DTIM
 ↪  DRET FLAGS
02:00:00:00:01:00 02:00:00:00:01:00 sta1-mp0 0   171     0    1504 0
 ↪  0                0x11
02:00:00:00:02:00 02:00:00:00:01:00 sta1-mp0 1   4268    0    1504 0
 ↪  0                0x15
```

This command prints the mesh paths as if they were a routing table linked to sta1. By observing this table, you can notice that the next hop (*NEXT HOP*) for sta2 (02:00:00:00:01:00) is sta2 itself, whereas the next hop for sta3 (02:00:00:00:02:00) is also sta2, since this node is located between sta1 and sta3.

Now close the Mininet-WiFi CLI and run *<adhoc.py>*.

```
mininet-wifi> exit
~/mininet-wifi$ sudo python mn-wifi-book-en/codes/cap3/adhoc.py
```

And then repeat the same communication process by connecting sta1 to sta2 and sta3, exactly as done previously.

```
mininet-wifi> sta1 ping -c1 sta2
PING 10.0.0.2 (10.0.0.2) 56(84) bytes of data.
64 bytes from 10.0.0.2: icmp_seq=1 ttl=64 time=2046 ms

--- 10.0.0.2 ping statistics ---
1 packets transmitted, 1 received, 0% packet loss, time 0ms
rtt min/avg/max/mdev = 2046.137/2046.137/2046.137/0.000 ms
mininet-wifi> sta1 ping -c1 sta3
PING 10.0.0.3 (10.0.0.3) 56(84) bytes of data.
From 10.0.0.1 icmp_seq=1 Destination Host Unreachable

--- 10.0.0.3 ping statistics ---
1 packets transmitted, 0 received, +1 errors, 100% packet loss, time 0ms
```

As we can see, sta1 cannot communicate with sta3, since sta2 was not instructed on how to forward data traffic to sta3 in order to allow sta1 and sta3 to establish communication with each other.

In wireless *ad hoc* networks, intermediate nodes do not automatically route traffic, as is done in wireless mesh networks. To do so, you first need to either setup a routing protocol or configure routing tables. So let us look at how this configuring can be done.

To do so, execute the following commands.

```
mininet-wifi> sta1 ip route add 10.0.0.3 via 10.0.0.2
mininet-wifi> sta3 ip route add 10.0.0.1 via 10.0.0.2
mininet-wifi> sta2 echo 1 > /proc/sys/net/ipv4/ip_forward
```

The first command instructs sta1 that, in case it needs to talk to sta3, the packet must first pass through sta2. The second, in turn, indicates that for the packet to arrive at sta1, from sta3, it must also pass through sta2. The third one instructs sta2 to forward packets addressed to sta1 and sta3.

Once all the necessary routing settings have been made, we can confirm them by viewing their routing tables, as follows.

```
mininet-wifi> sta1 route -n
Kernel IP routing table
Destination Gateway  Genmask         Flags Metric Ref  Use Iface
10.0.0.0    0.0.0.0  255.0.0.0       U     0      0      0 sta1-wlan0
10.0.0.3    10.0.0.2 255.255.255.255 UGH   0      0      0 sta1-wlan0
```

```
mininet-wifi> sta3 route -n
Kernel IP routing table
Destination Gateway  Genmask        Flags Metric Ref  Use Iface
10.0.0.0    0.0.0.0  255.0.0.0      U     0      0      0 sta3-wlan0
10.0.0.1    10.0.0.2 255.255.255.255 UGH  0      0      0 sta3-wlan0
```

Now, let us try again to *ping* between sta1 and sta3.

```
mininet-wifi> sta1 ping -c1 sta3
PING 10.0.0.3 (10.0.0.3) 56(84) bytes of data.
From 10.0.0.2: icmp_seq=1 Redirect Host(New nexthop: 10.0.0.3)
64 bytes from 10.0.0.3: icmp_seq=1 ttl=63 time=20.1 ms

--- 10.0.0.3 ping statistics ---
1 packets transmitted, 1 received, 0% packet loss, time 0ms
rtt min/avg/max/mdev = 20.167/20.167/20.167/0.000 ms
```

As you can see, communication can now be successfully established thanks to the static routing configured on the nodes.

 There are basically two types of routing: static and dynamic routing. Static routing is done similarly to the process performed above, using routes that are manually defined. Dynamic static, in turn, as the name itself indicates, is done dynamically, and in it the routing protocols are responsible for feeding the routing tables. Some of the main protocols that can be used for routing in wireless *ad hoc* networks are: AODV (*Ad hoc On demand Distance Vector*), OLSR (*Optimized Link State Routing*) and BATMAN (*Better Approach to Mobile Ad hoc Networking*).

 Mininet-WiFi: Understanding the difference between ad hoc and mesh wireless networks:
https://youtu.be/-1I-TuvsQ5s

Studies that previously used Mininet-WiFi for research on *ad hoc/mesh*:

- Venkatraman Balasubramanian, Ahmed Karmouch. *Managing the Mobile Ad-hoc Cloud Ecosystem using Software Defined Networking Principles*. International Symposium on Networks, Computers and Communications (ISNCC), 2017.
- A. S. AbdelRahman and A. B. El-Sisi. *Dynamic Load Balancing Technique for Software Defined WiFi Networks*. International Conference on Computer Engineering and Systems (ICCES), 2017.
- Hisham Elzain, Wu Yang. *Decentralizing Software-Defined Wireless Mesh Networking (D-SDWMN) Control Plane*. Proceedings of the World Congress on Engineering (WCE), 2018.
- Sachin Sharma and Maziar Nekovee. *A demonstration of automatic configuration of OpenFlow in wireless ad hoc networks*. International Conference on Computer Communication and Networks (ICCCN), 2019.

3.5 OpenFlow protocol

OpenFlow is a protocol focused primarily on the administration of LANs and WANs, with an emphasis on commercial equipment such as switches, routers, access points, etc. The fact that this protocol is a flexible and open standard gives it a prominent role, since it allows its users to have more freedom to innovate, especially with regard to academia and industry. The OpenFlow protocol also allows the reduction of costs needed for the maintenance of equipment, and makes the adoption of new business models possible.

Studies using the OpenFlow protocol are constantly developed and many extensions for it are proposed. Many of these proposals are related to wireless networks, mainly because the OpenFlow protocol was not originally designed for wireless networks.

In the following tutorials, we will learn about practical aspects of the Open-Flow protocol by analyzing some messages defined in its specification. It is important to note that the first version, 0.2.0, was released in May 2008 and is currently obsolete. The 1.0 version, released in December 2009, was the most used one and served as a basis for other versions, such as 1.1, 1.2, 1.3, 1.4 and 1.5. In addition to providing a set of functional enhancements to the protocol, new specification versions bring more header fields.

• Open Networking Foundation (ONF) Specifications. Available at: `https://www.opennetworking.org/software-defined-standards/specifications/`
• OpenFlow Protocol Decomposition. Available at: `http://flowgrammable.org/sdn/openflow/`
• Learn OpenFlow with Flowsim. Available at: `https://flowsim.flowgrammable.org/`
• Diego Kreutz, Fernando M. V. Ramos, Paulo Verissimo, Christian Esteve Rothenberg, Siamak Azodolmolky, Steve Uhlig. *Software-Defined Networking: A Comprehensive Survey*. In Proceedings of the IEEE, 2015. [12]

3.5.1 Capturing OpenFlow messages

 Requirement(s): *Wireshark*

Until now, the OpenFlow protocol has been explored in this book only theoretically, through descriptions of its conceptual aspects. However, it will be used in the majority of the tutorials in the remainder of this book. Therefore, because of its importance, we will learn a bit more about the operations of the OpenFlow protocol.

Unlike previous tutorials, let us start Mininet-WiFi with the simplest Mininet topology, which consists of two hosts, a switch and a controller. Next, we will use *Wireshark* to check a few messages related to this protocol.

```
~/mininet-wifi$ sudo mn
mininet-wifi> sh wireshark &
```

 As we have seen before, the *sudo mn* command creates a wired topology rather than a wireless one. We chose to create a wired topology because the OpenFlow protocol was not originally designed for wireless networks. Wireless networks have some peculiarities that we will discuss in section 3.5.3.

Once *Wireshark* is open, look for the word *any* on the interface list and initiate packet captures on this interface. Since OVS includes its own controller -

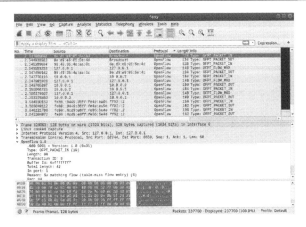

Figure 3.9: OpenFlow message capture.

ovs-testcontroller -, selecting the *any* option will allow you to capture any packet passing through your computer, including those targeting the OpenFlow controller.

Next, we will generate data traffic between h1 and h2, to allow us to analyze a few messages from the OpenFlow protocol, as shown in Figure 3.9.

```
mininet-wifi> h1 ping -c2 h2
PING 10.0.0.2 (10.0.0.2) 56(84) bytes of data.
64 bytes from 10.0.0.2: icmp_seq=1 ttl=64 time=10.1 ms
64 bytes from 10.0.0.2: icmp_seq=2 ttl=64 time=0.160 ms

--- 10.0.0.2 ping statistics ---
2 packets transmitted, 2 received, 0% packet loss, time 1001ms
rtt min/avg/max/mdev = 0.160/5.155/10.150/4.995 ms
```

Note that the response time to the first ICMP packet was much higher compared to the second. This is because of the discovery process. The steps regarding the communication process between h1 and h2 are described below and illustrated in Figure 3.10.

1. h1 sends an ARP/IMCP request in order to communicate with h2. This first packet enters the interface number one of switch s1.

2. Switch s1, in turn, does not know where h2 is located or even if it exists. Therefore, it must exchange a number of messages that result

in a longer response time to the first ICMP packet. Since it does not know what to do with the packet, s1 then forwards that packet to the controller (packet-in message) so that the controller can instruct the switch on what to do. Therefore, we can define the *packet-in* message as a message created by the switch that targets the controller.

3. The controller, in turn, responds to the switch with a *packet-out* message looking for the MAC address corresponding to h2's IP.

4. The switch then sends this broadcast message to all of its ports, except the port from which it received the h1 packet, since it already knows which node is connected to its number one port.

5. Host h2 then receives the message sent by the switch and returns it, making itself (h2) known by stating its own presence in the message.

6. The switch, which again does not know what to do with the message received by h2, since this message refers to the first packet received by the number two port of the switch. The switch then forwards the new packet-in message to the controller, which learns where h2 is located (switch port number two).

7. Thus, in response to this, the controller sends a *flow mod* message to the switch, instructing the switch to forward the packet received by h2 to h1.

8. Finally, the ICMP message is sent back to h1 in response format.

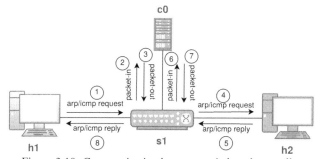

Figure 3.10: Communication between switch and controller.

To use the the OpenFlow protocol, it is critical to understand how it works. Its main difference in relation to the traditional model is that now there is the role of the controller, which centralizes the whole network communication process.

Alternatively, it is also possible to input manual instructions directly into either the switch or controller, thus preventing some types of messages from being exchanged among them. This process is very similar to the insertion of static routes in traditional routers when routing protocols are in use. When static rules are defined, we say that the switch is running in proactive mode. On the other hand, when it learns the rules, we say that it is working in reactive mode, as there is traffic on the network.

Turning now our attention to the issue about wireless networks, the reason we do not use the simplest topology of Mininet-WiFi is that access points have only one interface, the wireless interface, which can be associated with n stations. I.e. the same interface is used as an input and output for data traffic. In this situation there is a special treatment that must be used, which is defined in the OpenFlow protocol specification that will be explored in section 3.5.3.

 You can find more information about the OpenFlow protocol on the ONF (Open Network Foundation) website.

3.5.2 Creating flows

As discussed earlier, flows can be created dynamically or statically. These forms of flow insertion are known as reactive and proactive modes, respectively.

In this new tutorial we will explore these concepts and understand a bit more about how static rules work. To do so, let us start Mininet with a single-type topology consisting of four hosts, where all hosts are connected to the s1 switch, which in turn is connected to the c0 controller.

```
~/mininet-wifi$ sudo mn --topo single,4
```

Next, we check the switch table of switch s1 by running *ovs-ofctl*, a program that allows the managing of OpenFlow switches, especially those of the OVS type (*OpenVSwitch*).

```
mininet-wifi> sh ovs-ofctl dump-flows s1
NXST_FLOW reply (xid=0x4):
```

As a result of the command used above, switch s1 should not display any information about the flow table, since so far no packet has crossed switch s1.

So let us statically feed the flow table of switch s1. Since s1 is connected to an SDN controller, the controller itself would be able to respond to requests originating from s1. It is no wonder we have used the *ping* command successfully on several previous attempts. But since the purpose of this tutorial is to demonstrate how flows can be statically defined, let us do so.

In general, the rule below instructs the system that all packets entering port number one of switch s1 should exit through port number two. Moreover, all packets entering port number two must go out through port number one. I.e. the defined rule restricts, in this case, communication, allowing it to happen only between h1 and h2, since all packets that are created by these nodes must go out through the port to which the opposite node is connected.

```
mininet-wifi> sh ovs-ofctl add-flow s1 in_port=1,actions=output:2
mininet-wifi> sh ovs-ofctl add-flow s1 in_port=2,actions=output:1
```

Note that now you can observe the tables installed on switch s1 by issuing the *ovs-ofctl dump-flows* command.

```
mininet-wifi> sh ovs-ofctl dump-flows s1
  cookie=0x0, duration=7.553s, table=0, n_packets=1, n_bytes=70,
  ↪ in_port="s1-eth1" actions=output:"s1-eth2"
  cookie=0x0, duration=4.574s, table=0, n_packets=1, n_bytes=70,
  ↪ in_port="s1-eth2" actions=output:"s1-eth1"
```

In addition to this, you can also observe that there is communication between h1 and h2, as shown below. It is also important to remember that, according to the information described in the previous paragraph, both h3 and h4 cannot communicate with h1 and h2.

```
mininet-wifi> h1 ping -c1 h2
PING 10.0.0.2 (10.0.0.2) 56(84) bytes of data.
64 bytes from 10.0.0.2: icmp_seq=1 ttl=64 time=0.482 ms

--- 10.0.0.2 ping statistics ---
1 packets transmitted, 1 received, 0% packet loss, time 0ms
rtt min/avg/max/mdev = 0.482/0.482/0.482/0.000 ms
```

Now, let us disregard, for a moment, the previously established rules and create an action that causes the number three interface of switch s1 to ignore all incoming packets.

```
mininet-wifi> sh ovs-ofctl add-flow s1 in_port=3,actions=drop
```

And then we try a *ping* between h4 and h3.

```
mininet-wifi> h4 ping -c1 h3
PING 10.0.0.3 (10.0.0.3) 56(84) bytes of data.
From 10.0.0.4 icmp_seq=1 Destination Host Unreachable

--- 10.0.0.3 ping statistics ---
1 packets transmitted, 0 received, +1 errors, 100% packet loss, time 0ms
```

As you can see, an *action* called *drop* causes the packet to be discarded, thus rejecting communication with h3. In this particular case, h3 is completely isolated from the other nodes.

It is important to note that the rules are not limited to the port number. You can increment the rules with other information, such as the MAC address of sources and destinations, their IP address, protocol type, and many other options. A full list of possibilities can be found in the OpenFlow protocol specification on the ONF website.

 All of the rules described above were created using *ovs-ofctl*, a small program that lets you manage OpenVSwitch. Additionally, it is worth reading about *dpctl*, which can be used with both OpenVSwitch and BOFUSS (https://github.com/CPqD/ofsoftswitch13/).

3.5.3 OpenFlow and wireless networks

By default, access points are capable of forwarding packets that have the same incoming and outgoing port regardless of whether there are flows installed on it. However, the OpenFlow protocol specification says that packets entering and leaving the same port must be dropped.

The only way for a packet to not be rejected would be to instruct the access point on what to do with those packets that have the same input and output port. Obviously, instructing the access point on how to act in this situation would consequently inhibit the sending of packet-in messages to the controller, right?

In order to implement the OpenFlow protocol specification, let us start Mininet-WiFi with a new parameter, --no-bridge, which will allow communication to happen between sta1 and sta2 only if the access point was given an instruction authorizing communication between these two nodes.

To do so, run the following command.

```
~/mininet-wifi$ sudo mn --wifi --no-bridge
```

Then, try to start communication between sta1 and sta2 via *ping*.

```
mininet-wifi> sta1 ping -c5 sta2
PING 10.0.0.2 (10.0.0.2) 56(84) bytes of data.
From 10.0.0.1 icmp_seq=1 Destination Host Unreachable
From 10.0.0.1 icmp_seq=2 Destination Host Unreachable
From 10.0.0.1 icmp_seq=3 Destination Host Unreachable
From 10.0.0.1 icmp_seq=4 Destination Host Unreachable
From 10.0.0.1 icmp_seq=5 Destination Host Unreachable

--- 10.0.0.2 ping statistics ---
5 packets transmitted, 0 received, +5 errors, 100% packet loss, time 4100ms
```

As you can see, although both sta1 and sta2 were connected to the same access point, the communication between them was not successful.

As discussed earlier in this book, Mininet-WiFi uses the *hostapd* software for the virtualization of access points. One of the features of *hostapd* is to make communication possible only if the access points were instructed properly. The -- no-bridge command activates this function, and as at first there is no statement in ap1 indicating how sta1 can communicate with sta2, these nodes were unable to establish communication between themselves.

This information can be confirmed by running the *ovs-ofctl* program, as follows.

```
mininet-wifi> sh ovs-ofctl dump-flows ap1
NXST_FLOW reply (xid=0x4):
```

Therefore, you must add flow tables to access point ap1 in order to allow communication between sta1 and sta2 to occur. To do so, you will simply need to insert two rules, as can be seen below.

```
mininet-wifi> sh ovs-ofctl add-flow ap1 "priority=0,arp,in_port=1,
↪  actions=output:in_port"
mininet-wifi> sh ovs-ofctl add-flow ap1 "priority=0,icmp,in_port=1,
↪  actions=output:in_port"
```

What do the commands described above do? First, note that we are using *ovs-ofctl* again. Hence, you can use it to both view and install flows. In particular, the above commands instruct access point ap1 that every *arp* and *icmp* packets that enter through port number one must come out of ap1 itself, i.e. the ap1-wlan0 network interface, the same interface to which both sta1 and sta2 nodes are associated.

In case you did not understand, try imagining physical access points or wireless routers. Even though it has more than one antenna, the interface where all the mobile devices are associated with is unique, and all the packets come in and out through the same interface. This concept is the same used by Mininet-WiFi.

 The word "*sh*" must always be used on the Mininet-WiFi CLI when you need to execute a command not recognized by Mininet-WiFi, but by the operating system. Because *ovs-ofctl* is a software installed on the operating system, you must run it with *sh* on the Mininet-WiFi CLI. *The same command can be used outside the Mininet-WiFi CLI, without "sh".*

Now that we have instructed access point ap1 to behave properly when it receives a packet in its number one port, it will certainly be possible to *ping* successfully.

But first, let us see whether the rules were actually applied as expected.

```
mininet-wifi> sh ovs-ofctl dump-flows ap1
NXST_FLOW reply (xid=0x4):
cookie=0x0, duration=7.654s, table=0, n_packets=0, n_bytes=0, idle_age=7,
 ↪  priority=0,arp,in_port=1 actions=IN_PORT
cookie=0x0, duration=7.112s, table=0, n_packets=0, n_bytes=0, idle_age=7,
 ↪  priority=0,icmp,in_port=1 actions=IN_PORT
```

Once the appropriate application of the rules has been confirmed, a further *ping* attempt between sta1 and sta2 can be performed.

```
mininet-wifi> sta1 ping -c1 sta2
PING 10.0.0.2 (10.0.0.2) 56(84) bytes of data.
64 bytes from 10.0.0.2: icmp_seq=1 ttl=64 time=1.08 ms

--- 10.0.0.2 ping statistics ---
1 packets transmitted, 1 received, 0% packet loss, time 0ms
rtt min/avg/max/mdev = 1.082/1.082/1.082/0.000 ms
```

As you can see, the attempt to communicate using *ping* has finally been successful thanks to the rules defined for access point ap1.

 The ovs-ofctl show ap1 command can be used to identify ap1's port numbers and ensure the use of the correct port number.

3.5.4 Remote controller

 Requirement(s): *Ryu*

In the tutorials we completed so far, you ran the controller on your computer and in a somewhat abstract way. To be more precise, we started Mininet-WiFi and the controller was started along with it. However, in the real world the controller is installed and runs on a known computer or server.

So, let us run a test with a controller other than *ovs-testcontroller*: the Ryu controller. Although the official controller repository is located at https://github.com/osrg/ryu, we will use for the following tutorials in this book a fork of the official repository, which is available at https://github.com/ramonfontes/ryu. More specifically, we will consider the *book branch*.

Therefore, you will need to make a copy of the *Ryu* source code from this repository and *branch*. For standardization and organization purposes we recommend cloning the *Ryu* code into the Mininet-WiFi directory as follows.

```
~/mininet-wifi$ git clone https://github.com/ramonfontes/ryu -b book
~/mininet-wifi$ cd ryu
```

Although the *Ryu* controller is used as an external controller in this book, most of its tutorials should work normally with any other controller, such as OpenDayLight, Floodlight, and so on. The only exceptions are the tutorials that require Ryu's source code to be modified, as is the case with the tutorial for vehicular networks.

 What is the best OpenFlow controller? This is a very particular question, whose answer will depend substantially on the purpose for which you intend to use it. Issues such as the programming language the controller was developed in and availability of supported versions of the OpenFlow protocol should be factored into your decision process.

Let us then continue this tutorial by executing the following command. The sudo mn command has been described previously; however, now we will use it alongside the --controller parameter.

```
~/mininet-wifi$ sudo mn --controller=remote
```

What the --controller basically does is indicate that a remote controller should be used, otherwise the network will not work as expected. What does this mean? For example, if a *ping* attempt is made between h1 and h2, you can notice that these nodes are unable to communicate with each other, resulting in 100% packet loss.

```
mininet-wifi> h1 ping -c1 h2
PING 10.0.0.2 (10.0.0.2) 56(84) bytes of data.
From 10.0.0.1 icmp_seq=1 Destination Host Unreachable

--- 10.0.0.2 ping statistics ---
1 packets transmitted, 0 received, +1 errors, 100% packet loss, time 0ms
```

Therefore, you must start a remote controller so that the nodes can communicate with each other. To do so, try running *Ryu* on a new terminal. As you have previously acquired the *Ryu* source code, it can be started as follows.

```
~/mininet-wifi/ryu$ sudo PYTHONPATH=. ./bin/ryu-manager
↪ ryu/app/simple_switch_13.py
```

And then a new attempt to *ping* can be made between h1 and h2.

```
mininet-wifi> h1 ping -c1 h2
PING 10.0.0.2 (10.0.0.2) 56(84) bytes of data.
64 bytes from 10.0.0.2: icmp_seq=1 ttl=64 time=1023 ms

--- 10.0.0.2 ping statistics ---
1 packets transmitted, 1 received, 0% packet loss, time 0ms
rtt min/avg/max/mdev = 1023.761/1023.761/1023.761/0.000 ms
```

Now, as you can see, h1 was able to communicate with h2, which shows how important the controller is for the full operation of the OpenFlow network.

3.5.5 OpenFlow and handover

 Requirement(s): script(s) only

Handover or *handoff* (as preferred in Europe) refers to the process used in wireless networks, Wi-Fi or not, to carry out the transition of a station from one cell to another in a way that is transparent to the user.

Imagine that you are holding your smartphone, and while you are watching a video, regardless of the signal range of the access points available at the company you work in or on a university campus, they have been so well distributed that you remain connected at all times. And this happens mainly because of the process called handover.

In this tutorial, we will describe the handover process and observe an important issue regarding handover and the OpenFlow protocol, which many users end up facing and at first do not know the reason why. To do so, we will run *<handover.py>*, which includes a topology similar to the one shown in Figure 3.11.

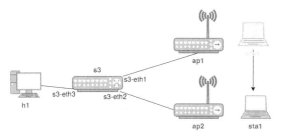

Figure 3.11: Handover topology.

```
~/mininet-wifi$ sudo python mn-wifi-book-en/codes/cap3/handover.py
```

Then, on the Mininet-WiFi CLI try to *ping* between h1 and sta1.

```
mininet-wifi> h1 ping -c5 sta1
PING 10.0.0.1 (10.0.0.1) 56(84) bytes of data.
64 bytes from 10.0.0.1: icmp_seq=1 ttl=64 time=46.5 ms
64 bytes from 10.0.0.1: icmp_seq=2 ttl=64 time=1.48 ms
64 bytes from 10.0.0.1: icmp_seq=3 ttl=64 time=1.17 ms
64 bytes from 10.0.0.1: icmp_seq=4 ttl=64 time=1.17 ms
64 bytes from 10.0.0.1: icmp_seq=5 ttl=64 time=1.18 ms

--- 10.0.0.1 ping statistics ---
5 packets transmitted, 5 received, 0% packet loss, time 4005ms
rtt min/avg/max/mdev = 1.175/10.319/46.574/18.127 ms
```

As you can see, sta1 can communicate with h1 and vice versa. Note that sta1 is initially associated with access point ap1.

Now, let us change the position of station sta1, so that it stays under the signal range of ap2 and consequently associates with it.

```
mininet-wifi> py sta1.setPosition('60,10,0')
```

Then try again to *ping* between h1 and sta1.

```
mininet-wifi> sta1 ping -c5 h1
PING 10.0.0.2 (10.0.0.2) 56(84) bytes of data.

--- 10.0.0.2 ping statistics ---
5 packets transmitted, 0 received, 100% packet loss, time 4074ms
```

Why is it that sta1 can no longer communicate with h1? Because the way the controller acted made it impossible for communication between sta1 and h1 to take place. What does that mean? Before answering this question, let us check the connections between the access points and the switch.

```
mininet-wifi> links
sta1-wlan0<->wifi (OK wifi)
ap1-eth2<->s3-eth1 (OK OK)
ap2-eth2<->s3-eth2 (OK OK)
s3-eth3<->h1-eth0 (OK OK)
```

Now, let us look at the flow table of switch s3.

```
mininet-wifi> sh ovs-ofctl dump-flows s3
 cookie=0x0, duration=49.302s, table=0, n_packets=4, n_bytes=392,
 ↪ idle_timeout=60, priority=65535, icmp, in_port="s3-eth1",
 ↪ vlan_tci=0x0000, dl_src=02:00:00:00:00:00, dl_dst=e2:8f:ac:bd:6c:79,
 ↪ nw_src=10.0.0.1, nw_dst=10.0.0.2, nw_tos=0, icmp_type=8, icmp_code=0
 ↪ actions=output:"s3-eth3"
 cookie=0x0, duration=49.299s, table=0, n_packets=9, n_bytes=882,
 ↪ idle_timeout=60, priority=65535 ,icmp,in_port="s3-eth3",
 ↪ vlan_tci=0x0000, dl_src=e2:8f:ac:bd:6c:79,
 ↪ dl_dst=02:00:00:00:00:00,nw_src=10.0.0.2, nw_dst=10.0.0.1, nw_tos=0,
 ↪ icmp_type=0, icmp_code=0 actions=output:"s3-eth1"
 cookie=0x0, duration=24.518s, table=0, n_packets=4, n_bytes=392,
 ↪ idle_timeout=60, priority=65535, icmp, in_port="s3-eth2",
 ↪ vlan_tci=0x0000, dl_src=02:00:00:00:00:00, dl_dst=e2:8f:ac:bd:6c:79,
 ↪ nw_src=10.0.0.1, nw_dst=10.0.0.2, nw_tos=0, icmp_type=8, icmp_code=0
 ↪ actions=output:"s3-eth3"
```

The first part of the output represents a flow installed on the switch s3. It says that any packet that goes to the s3-eth1 interface should be forwarded to s3-eth3. The second part says that any packet that goes to interface s3-eth3 must exit through s3-eth1. Until then, there is a perfect communication going on between ap1 and s3, whose origin is sta1 and destination is h1, correct?

 Part of the output from *dump-flows* has been omitted so that we can focus more specifically on what interests us: the communication between sta1 and sta2.

Now let us look at the third and last flow. What does it say? It says that packets entering interface s3-eth2 must go out through interface s3-eth3. It is very similar to the first packet, changing only the input interface. In this case, the packet arrives at the s3 switch, which in turn routes the packet to host h1 (*echo request*).

What about the *echo reply*? What happens when the packet needs to be returned to sta1? The s3 switch will continue trying to forward the packet to the station via ap1, since there is still a flow table with this statement, despite sta1 no longer being associated with access point ap1, which makes it so that no communication is possible.

So, what could be done to make communication between sta1 and h1 possible? There are controllers that were developed to handle this specific situation. The Odin controller[4], for instance, promises mobility management. However, as a workaround, we could fix this issue by using a home-made solution.

What happens is that if the switch does not receive any packet for sixty seconds, it will erase the existing entries and sta1 will be able to communicate with h1 again. Simple, right? A sixty second duration is set in *idle_timeout* (see the flows shown above). Thus, if the switch does not receive packets that match the previously-installed flow - whose source is h1 and destination sta1 -, it will simply erase that input from its flow table.

Somewhat similar to *idle_timeout* is *hard_timeout*. However, in *hard_timeout*, entries are excluded regardless of the presence of new matching packets. But back to the case in question: would you prefer to wait a minute to make another attempt at communication? Certainly not.

Therefore, in order to not have to wait for sixty seconds, you can delete the previously installed table. For example, the command below will erase any flow that has as its reference point the s3-eth3 input port, from the s3 switch interface that is connected to host h1.

```
mininet-wifi> sh ovs-ofctl del-flows s3 "in_port=s3-eth3"
```

---

[4]https://github.com/Wi5/odin-wi5-controller

After this, sta1 will finally be able to reestablish communication with h1.

```
mininet-wifi> sta1 ping -c1 h1
PING 10.0.0.2 (10.0.0.2) 56(84) bytes of data.
64 bytes from 10.0.0.2: icmp_seq=1 ttl=64 time=17.8 ms

--- 10.0.0.2 ping statistics ---
1 packets transmitted, 1 received, 0% packet loss, time 0ms
rtt min/avg/max/mdev = 17.846/17.846/17.846/0.000 ms
```

Another alternative to solve this problem would be to identify the input packets on the s3-eth3 interface and create an action called normal, which is available in the OpenFlow protocol and is used to make the switch operate as a traditional switch.

 What would happen if both *idle_timeout* and *hard_timeout* were set to the same value? *Hard_timeout* would occur and flows would be excluded regardless of the presence of new packets.

3.6 Use case scenarios

From now on we will perform some common scenario tutorials on computer networks that support Mininet-WiFi. These scenarios include web servers, DHCP, *firewall*, among other networks.

3.6.1 WEB server

 Requirement(s): *SimpleHTTPServer*

Web servers are some of the most widely used services and servers in the world and are essential for a website to be available on the internet. They basically consist of computers that host one or more internet sites or programs or even local area networks. The term web server, however, may refer to both the hardware and software.

In this tutorial we will run a web server from one node in Mininet-WiFi and access the content of the tutorial through another one. To do so we will use *SimpleHTTPServer*. *SimpleHTTPServer* is a module of the *Python* programming language that functions as a simple and fast alternative to serve files from a directory on the local system via HTTP and without having to install other web servers such as Apache, Nginx, and so on.

Although it is a prerequisite, *SimpleHTTPServer* should already be installed on your system, since *Python* is also installed and this module is part of version 2.x of *Python*.

 If you have *Python* 3.x installed and want to use a module for web servers, you should use *http.server*, since this new module replaces *SimpleHTTPServer* in version 3.x.

To explore *SimpleHTTPServer*, let us first start Mininet-WiFi with its simplest topology.

```
~/mininet-wifi$ sudo mn --wifi
```

Then, we start *SimpleHTTPServer* on sta1 as below.

```
mininet-wifi> sta1 python -m SimpleHTTPServer 80 &
```

Next, we use sta2 to consume the content of *SimpleHTTPServer* that is stored in sta1.

```
mininet-wifi> sta2 wget -O - sta1
```

A result similar to the one given below should be seen.

```
--2018-12-26 13:38:34--  http://10.0.0.1/
Connecting to 10.0.0.1:80... connected.
HTTP request sent, awaiting response... 200 OK
Length: 4780 (4,7K) [text/html]
Saving to: 'STDOUT'
 ...
 ...
-    100%[===================>]   4,67K  --.-KB/s    in 0,002s
```

Although this is only a simple test, it can be used as a support for more sophisticated tests, where, for instance, the transfer time of a given file could be measured in different circumstances, such as background traffic, mobility, etc.

Local files can also be accessed by replacing the destination with the IP address. For example, assuming that there is a text file called <*test.txt*>, it can be accessed as follows:

```
mininet-wifi> sta2 wget -O - 10.0.0.1/test.txt
```

The <*test.txt*> file was not previously created for this tutorial, but you can do so. It is important to note that the file must be saved in the directory from which *SimpleHTTPServer* is ran.

3.6.2 DHCP server

  Requirement(s): *isc-dhcp-server*

The DHCP protocol (*Dynamic Host Configuration Protocol*) is one of the most important services in the network infrastructure. It is responsible for assigning IP addresses dynamically, so that you do not need to alter the machine's settings to connect to the network.

In general, you can assign IP addresses in three different ways:

Dynamic - the most common method, because, in it, the DHCP server provides the network settings. However, these are not permanent, and after a certain period, usually after the client machine is shut down or restarted, the addressing is updated;
Automatic - similar to the dynamic configuration; its main difference is that it will make the DHCP server provide the same address used in the last request;
Manual - the administrator binds the MAC address of the client device to a specific IP address.

In this tutorial, we will understand how a DHCP server works, from its configuration process to its execution, also analyzing the exchange of messages between server and client afterwards. To accomplish this, we will first execute the <*dhcp.py*> file, which generates a topology similar to the one shown in Figure 3.12.

```
~/mininet-wifi$ sudo python mn-wifi-book-en/codes/cap3/dhcp.py
```

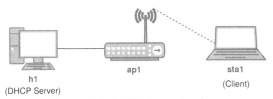

h1
(DHCP Server)

ap1

sta1
(Client)

Figure 3.12: DHCP Server topology.

 <*dhcp.py*> includes three parameters that need to be explained. The *failMode='standalone'* parameter makes the access point work as a traditional access point; *inNamespace=False* causes the host h1 to be executed in the root network namespace, instead of running in a namespace by itself; and the *echo 1 > /proc/sys/net/ipv4/ip_forward* command enables the IP forwarding on h1.

After running the script you can see that sta1 has no IP address. The reason for this is simple: the DHCP server has not been properly configured yet.

```
mininet-wifi> sta1 ip add show
1: lo: <LOOPBACK,UP,LOWER_UP> mtu 65536 qdisc noqueue state UNKNOWN group
↪ default qlen 1000
    link/loopback 00:00:00:00:00:00 brd 00:00:00:00:00:00
    inet 127.0.0.1/8 scope host lo
    valid_lft forever preferred_lft forever
    inet6 ::1/128 scope host
    valid_lft forever preferred_lft forever
354: sta1-wlan0: <NO-CARRIER,BROADCAST,MULTICAST,UP,LOWER_UP> mtu 1500
↪ qdisc mq state DORMANT group default qlen 1000
    link/ether 00:00:00:00:00:12 brd ff:ff:ff:ff:ff:ff
```

Hence, to assign an IP address for sta1 you will need to configure a DHCP server first. To do so, you will need to install a program that will act as a DHCP server, such as *isc-dhcp-server*. We will install it using the following command:

```
~/mininet-wifi$ sudo apt install isc-dhcp-server
```

Once *isc-dhcp-server* is installed, you will need to configure the configuration file located at *</etc/dhcp/dhcpd.conf>* (*the location of the file may vary depending on the version of the DHCP server being used*). To configure it, we suggest first accessing the dhcp directory and then copying the *<dhcpd.conf>* file, for security reasons.

```
~/mininet-wifi$ cd /etc/dhcp
~/etc/dhcp$ cp dhcpd.conf dhcpd.conf.bkp
```

You then need to edit *<dhcpd.conf>* and copy the content below and paste it into the file's text. *<dhcpd.conf>* can be edited using your preferred text editor.

```
option domain-name-servers 192.168.11.1;
subnet 192.168.11.0 netmask 255.255.255.0 {
range 192.168.11.2 192.168.11.254;
option routers 192.168.11.1;
default-lease-time 6000;
max-lease-time 72000;
INTERFACES="h1-eth0";
}
```

Following all of the above steps, let us open a terminal for h1 and another for sta1.

```
mininet-wifi> xterm sta1 h1
```

Then locate the h1 terminal and restart the DHCP server to apply the new settings by executing the following command.

```
h1# service isc-dhcp-server restart
```

Now, let us perform two tasks on the sta1 terminal: the first one is to start *Wireshark* and check the exchange of messages between the DHCP server and the client; and the second one is to have sta1 search for the IP address that will be assigned by h1, i.e. the DHCP server.

```
sta1# wireshark &
```

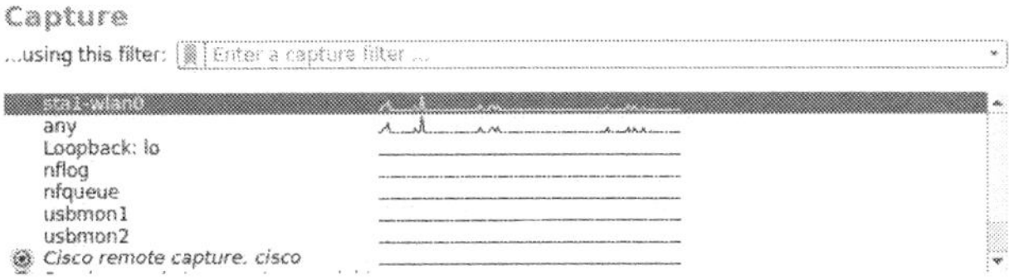

Figure 3.13: Interface sta1-wlan0 from sta1.

When issued, the "&" character runs *Wireshark* and allows you to execute new commands on the same terminal. With *Wireshark*, find the sta1-wlan0 interface and start capturing through it, as shown in Figure 3.13.

Then, returning to the sta1 terminal, let us assign an IP address to it using the *dhclient* command.

```
sta1# dhclient
```

Finally, check the IP address assigned to sta1. If everything happened as expected, you will be to see an IP address on the 192.168.11.0/24 subnet assigned to sta1 (see Figure 3.14).

Now, using *Wireshark* again, you can notice that the it shows four important messages, which are part of the IP address assignment process. These messages are: DHCP Discover, DHCP Offer, DHCP Request and DHCP ACK.

Generally speaking, the previously performed DHCP service functioned as follows:
- Initially, sta1 sent a UDP packet called DHCP Discover to all network devices. If there were more nodes connected to access point ap1, the other nodes would also receive a copy of the packet;
- The computer responsible for the DHCP service - h1 -, in turn, responded to DHCP Discover by providing the IP address to the sta1 client. This step is carried out by DHCP Offer;
- Then, after receiving the DHCP Offer packet, sta1 sent another packet to the server that requested a "lease" of the information previously

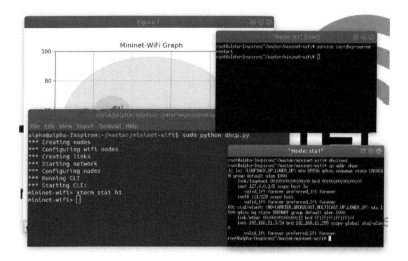

Figure 3.14: DHCP Server running.

provided by the DHCP server. This packet (or message) is called DHCP Request;

• Finally, after receiving the DHCP Request packet from the client, the DHCP server confirmed receipt of the "lease" request by sending the DHCP ACK message.

 If sta1 has not received an IP address and/or could not view the messages on Wireshark, we recommend that you restart your system. Ensure that the 192.168.11.0/24 subnet has not been previously configured on your system, otherwise you may need to make changes in the *<dhcpd.conf* file>.

3.6.3 Dealing with loops

 Requirement(s): script(s) only

A switching loop occurs when there is more than one layer 2 path between two endpoint devices. In other words, there are several connections between two switches or two ports that are linked together on the same switch. The problem is that when there is a switching loop in the network, the destination will be inaccessible until the switching loop disappears.

Switching loops also generate broadcast storms, since broadcast packets are routed to all ports on the switch. As a consequence, the switch will repeatedly re-transmit the broadcast messages, flooding the entire network and causing loss of communication between the devices that comprise it.
In this tutorial we will see a practical example of the switching loop and how it can be avoided. To do this, we will run <*loop.py*>. The topology provided by this script retracts the previously used topology, shown in Figure 3.15. Note that to reach sta2, a packet generated by sta1 can be forwarded through two paths: either via sta3 or directly to sta2.

```
~/mininet-wifi$ sudo python mn-wifi-book-en/codes/cap3/loop.py
```

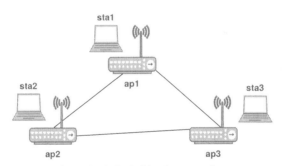

Figure 3.15: Switching loop topology.

Then, try to *ping* between sta1 and sta2.

```
mininet-wifi> sta1 ping -c1 sta2
PING 10.0.0.2 (10.0.0.2) 56(84) bytes of data.
From 10.0.0.1 icmp_seq=1 Destination Host Unreachable

--- 10.0.0.2 ping statistics ---
1 packets transmitted, 0 received, +1 errors, 100% packet loss, time 0ms
```

As you can see, *ping* was not successful. One of the ways to avoid layer 2 loops is by using the Spanning-Tree Protocol (STP). Basically, the STP blocks redundant paths, thus avoiding the formation of loops. In fact, it is precisely because of this behavior (path blocking) that in some networks (data centers, for example) the STP is not very well accepted.

To check the STP in action, close Mininet-WiFi and run the same script as before, with -*s*.

```
mininet-wifi> exit
~/mininet-wifi$ sudo python mn-wifi-book-en/codes/cap3/loop.py -s
```

Then, on the Mininet-WiFi CLI, do the operation indicated by the method below. This method will inform when the convergence of the STP has been completed. A message stating "True" should appear, indicating convergence.

```
mininet-wifi> py net.waitConnected()
*** Waiting for switches/aps to connect
ap3 ap1 ap2
True
```

Finally, try a new *ping* between sta1 and sta2.

```
mininet-wifi> sta1 ping -c1 sta2
PING 10.0.0.2 (10.0.0.2) 56(84) bytes of data.
64 bytes from 10.0.0.2: icmp_seq=1 ttl=64 time=2.48 ms

--- 10.0.0.2 ping statistics ---
1 packets transmitted, 1 received, 0% packet loss, time 0ms
rtt min/avg/max/mdev = 2.489/2.489/2.489/0.000 ms
```

As you can notice, *ping* has now been successful thanks to the STP protocol.

The following command confirms that the STP protocol is indeed active.

```
mininet-wifi> sh ovs-ofctl show ap1
OFPT_FEATURES_REPLY (xid=0x2): dpid:1000000000000001
n_tables:254, n_buffers:0
capabilities: FLOW_STATS TABLE_STATS PORT_STATS QUEUE_STATS ARP_MATCH_IP
actions: output enqueue set_vlan_vid set_vlan_pcp strip_vlan mod_dl_src
 ↪  mod_dl_dst mod_nw_src mod_nw_dst mod_nw_tos mod_tp_src mod_tp_dst
 1(ap1-wlan1): addr:02:00:00:00:03:00
     config:    0
     state:     STP_FORWARD
     speed: 0 Mbps now, 0 Mbps max
 2(ap1-eth2): addr:ee:74:8c:50:a5:0d
     config:    0
```

```
     state:    STP_FORWARD
     current:  10GB-FD COPPER
     speed: 10000 Mbps now, 0 Mbps max
  3(ap1-eth3): addr:8a:b3:aa:0a:95:5f
     config:   0
     state:    STP_FORWARD
     current:  10GB-FD COPPER
     speed: 10000 Mbps now, 0 Mbps max
  LOCAL(ap1): addr:46:1a:2c:d4:84:4e
     config:   PORT_DOWN
     state:    LINK_DOWN
     speed: 0 Mbps now, 0 Mbps max
  OFPT_GET_CONFIG_REPLY (xid=0x4): frags=normal miss_send_len=0
```

3.6.4 Virtual LAN (VLAN)

 Requirement(s): *bridge-utils, vlan*

Virtual Local Area Networks (VLANs) are local networks that organize a set of computers in a logical way, where communication between the various computers is managed by the physical architecture. Thanks to the freedom brought by virtual networks (VLANs), it is possible to get rid of the physical architecture's limitations, such as geographic or even addressing restrictions. This allows the definition of a logical segmentation based on a grouping of machines, also due to criteria that permit the use of MAC addresses, port numbers, protocols, and so on. Even in the simplest VLAN configuration, the user can define different VLAN IDs for different groups of devices and reduce the size of the broadcast domain in order to improve network quality.

In this tutorial we will segment the network using VLANs. The goal is to separate stations that are associated with different access points and still perform a number of configurations that will allow communication between the stations that belong to different VLANs.

Before starting this tutorial, you will need to install a few packages. The following command should install all necessary packages.

```
~/mininet-wifi$ sudo apt install bridge-utils vlan
```

Now, let us run <*vlan.py*>. The topology included in this script consists of four stations and two access points, arranged and configured according to Figure 3.16

```
~/mininet-wifi$ sudo python mn-wifi-book-en/codes/cap3/vlan.py
```

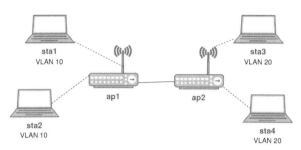

Figure 3.16: VLANs topology.

After running <*vlan.py*>, we will try to *ping* between sta1 and sta2.

```
mininet-wifi> sta1 ping -c1 sta2
PING 10.0.0.2 (10.0.0.2) 56(84) bytes of data.
64 bytes from 10.0.0.2: icmp_seq=1 ttl=64 time=0.344 ms

--- 10.0.0.2 ping statistics ---
1 packets transmitted, 1 received, 0% packet loss, time 0ms
rtt min/avg/max/mdev = 0.344/0.344/0.344/0.000 ms
```

Now, ping between sta1 and sta3.

```
mininet-wifi> sta1 ping -c1 sta3
PING 10.0.0.3 (10.0.0.3) 56(84) bytes of data.
From 10.0.0.1 icmp_seq=1 Destination Host Unreachable

--- 10.0.0.3 ping statistics ---
1 packets transmitted, 0 received, +1 errors, 100% packet loss, time 0ms
```

Both sta1 and sta3 are configured to operate on separate VLANs. For this reason and due to the lack of instructions given to access points ap1 and ap2 - which could allow communication between sta1 and sta3 to happen -, they cannot communicate with each other.

Now let us assume that it is necessary to allow communication between nodes belonging to different VLANs. Therefore, we will need to create instructions that will enable this communication. To do so, we will create the rules using the OpenFlow protocol. The four rules below modify the VLAN number (or VLAN ID), thus allowing communication to take place between all the nodes that comprise the topology, including those belonging to different VLANs.

```
mininet-wifi> sh ovs-ofctl add-flow ap1
 ↪ priority=100,in_port=1,dl_vlan=10,actions=mod_vlan_vid:20,output:2
mininet-wifi> sh ovs-ofctl add-flow ap1
 ↪ priority=100,in_port=2,dl_vlan=20,actions=mod_vlan_vid:10,output:1
mininet-wifi> sh ovs-ofctl add-flow ap2
 ↪ priority=100,in_port=1,dl_vlan=20,actions=mod_vlan_vid:10,output:2
mininet-wifi> sh ovs-ofctl add-flow ap2
 ↪ priority=100,in_port=2,dl_vlan=10,actions=mod_vlan_vid:20,output:1
```

Now, let us repeat the attempt to *ping* sta1 and sta3.

```
mininet-wifi> sta1 ping -c1 sta3
PING 10.0.0.3 (10.0.0.3) 56(84) bytes of data.
64 bytes from 10.0.0.3: icmp_seq=1 ttl=64 time=1.75 ms

--- 10.0.0.3 ping statistics ---
1 packets transmitted, 1 received, 0% packet loss, time 0ms
rtt min/avg/max/mdev = 1.751/1.751/1.751/0.000 ms
```

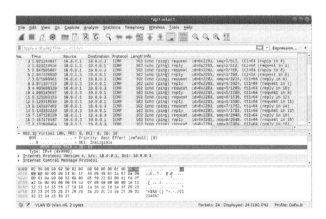

Figure 3.17: VLAN ID captured from ap1-wlan0.

As you can notice, the communication between sta1 and sta3 was successfully established because of the four rules, which correctly applied to access points ap1 and ap2. Consequently, *Wireshark* can be used to verify information about the VLAN ID, as shown in Figure 3.17.

VLAN striping

  Requirement(s): *bridge-utils, vlan*

Now, let us carry out a slightly different procedure than the one we did before. Let us make it so that the number ten VLAN is untagged when it leaves sta1's interface, and tagged when it enters the same interface.

First, let us remove any existing VLAN markup. In the example below we use ip link, but you can also use vconfig, a program for configuring VLANs.

```
mininet-wifi> sta3 ip link delete sta3-wlan0.20
mininet-wifi> sta4 ip link delete sta4-wlan0.20
mininet-wifi> sta3 ip link set sta3-wlan0 down
mininet-wifi> sta4 ip link set sta4-wlan0 down
mininet-wifi> sta3 ip link set sta3-wlan0 up
mininet-wifi> sta4 ip link set sta4-wlan0 up
mininet-wifi> sta3 iw dev sta3-wlan0 connect ssid-ap2
mininet-wifi> sta4 iw dev sta4-wlan0 connect ssid-ap2
```

Note that it was necessary to do a manual association with ap2, since the ip link command includes another that disables the wireless interface of both sta3 and sta4 via the *down* parameter.

Once the association is made, note that sta1 is again unable to communicate with sta3, since there is no VLAN defined for sta3.

```
mininet-wifi> sta1 ping -c1 sta3
PING 10.0.0.3 (10.0.0.3) 56(84) bytes of data.
From 10.0.0.1 icmp_seq=1 Destination Host Unreachable

--- 10.0.0.3 ping statistics ---
1 packets transmitted, 0 received, +1 errors, 100% packet loss, time 0ms
```

Now, let us enable VLAN untagging again using the OpenFlow protocol.

```
mininet-wifi> sh ovs-ofctl add-flow ap1
↪ priority=100,in_port=1,dl_vlan=10,actions=strip_vlan,output:2
mininet-wifi> sh ovs-ofctl add-flow ap1
↪ priority=100,in_port=2,actions=mod_vlan_vid:10,output:1
```

Finally, do a new *ping* attempt in order to communicate. If all was set up properly, it should be successful again.

```
mininet-wifi> sta1 ping -c1 sta3
PING 10.0.0.3 (10.0.0.3) 56(84) bytes of data.
64 bytes from 10.0.0.3: icmp_seq=1 ttl=64 time=0.456 ms

--- 10.0.0.3 ping statistics ---
1 packets transmitted, 1 received, 0% packet loss, time 0ms
rtt min/avg/max/mdev = 0.456/0.456/0.456/0.000 ms
```

VLAN tagging and untagging is not limited to the OpenFlow protocol. Any other network command executable on Linux operating systems can also be used.

3.6.5 Routing

Routing is the name given to the process of choosing among several possible ways to send a message. The node that makes this choice is called a router. There are basically two ways to perform MAC/IP routing: through static routing and/or dynamic routing. In the following tutorials, we will discuss a little more about these two types of routing.

Static routing

 Requirement(s): script(s) only

In static routing, the network administrator is responsible for manually completing the route table (creation and change). This type of routing is typically used in networks with few connection elements and is relatively simple to configure in small networks. On the other hand, its maintenance is relatively difficult in medium and large networks.

In this tutorial, we will enable communication between two nodes that are separated by two wireless routers, exactly as illustrated in Figure 3.18. To do so, let us run *<static-routing.py>*.

```
~/mininet-wifi$ sudo python mn-wifi-book-en/codes/cap3/static-routing.py
```

Afterwards, let us try a *ping* between sta1 and sta2.

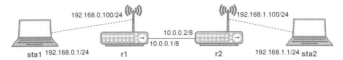

Figure 3.18: Static routing topology.

```
mininet-wifi> sta1 ping -c1 sta2
PING 192.168.1.1 (192.168.1.1) 56(84) bytes of data.
From 192.168.0.100 icmp_seq=1 Destination Net Unreachable

--- 192.168.1.1 ping statistics ---
1 packets transmitted, 0 received, +1 errors, 100% packet loss, time 0ms
```

As you can see, sta1 cannot communicate with sta2, even though the gateway address is set. You might wonder, then: what could be happening? What
could be preventing communication between sta1 and sta2?

By making a brief analysis, it is possible to observe that the r1 router knows
192.168.0.0/24 and 10.0.0.0/8, while the r2 router knows 192.168.1.0/24 and
also 10.0.0.0/8, since these IPs are directly connected to these routers (see
Figure 3.18). I.e. router r1 does not know the existence of 192.168.1.0/24 or
how to get on its network, especially with regard to the sta2 station, whose IP
is 192.168.1.1. Router r2, on the other hand, does not know on how to acquire
192.168.0.0/24, especially regarding station sta1, whose IP is 192.168.0.1/24.

Therefore, you need to create a route table to solve this deadlock and allow communication to happen among the nodes. The commands below will
cause r1 and r2 to know the networks previously unknown to them, or more
specifically the hosts that are unreachable.

```
mininet-wifi> r1 ip route add to 192.168.1.1 via 10.0.0.2
mininet-wifi> r2 ip route add to 192.168.0.1 via 10.0.0.1
```

Then, let us finally try a new *ping* between sta1 and sta2.

```
mininet-wifi> sta1 ping -c1 sta2
PING 192.168.1.1 (192.168.1.1) 56(84) bytes of data.
64 bytes from 192.168.1.1: icmp_seq=1 ttl=62 time=0.122 ms

--- 192.168.1.1 ping statistics ---
1 packets transmitted, 1 received, 0% packet loss, time 0ms
rtt min/avg/max/mdev = 0.122/0.122/0.122/0.000 ms
```

As you can see, *ping* was successful.

Now, picture the Internet, which has thousands of routers and paths often arranged in an unorganized way, where each company is responsible for its equipment. Creating static routes for each router would be very costly and difficult to maintain. Thus, it is often necessary to configure dynamic routes through routing protocols. Then, given its importance, let us understand how dynamic routing works.

Dynamic routing

 Requirement(s): script(s) only

Usually, modern computer networks use dynamic routing algorithms instead of static routing. The routing algorithms are implemented by the protocols, commonly known as routing protocols. These protocols are divided into two main groups: distance vector and link state. The first group tracks the number of hops, or routers existing between source and destination, as a metric. The second group registers, also as a metric, the state of the network, which can include traffic load, bandwidth, the cost of the circuit, the service priority assigned to the packets that are created or forwarded to a specific point, among other variables.

For this tutorial, we will use a program that simulates the RIP routing protocol (*Routing Information Protocol*), a distance vector protocol. The scripts used in this tutorial were created by *Peter L Dordal*, author of the book "*An Introduction to Computer Networks*". Although they are currently available on the Internet[5], you may need to read the book for more information should the public link be altered or made unavailable.

As the *book* repository already includes all the scripts and codes needed, let us then run this tutorial's script.

```
~/mininet-wifi$ sudo python mn-wifi-book-en/codes/cap3/routerline.py
```

---

[5]http://intronetworks.cs.luc.edu/current/html/mininet.html# ip-routers-with-simple-distance-vector-implementation

As illustrated in Figure 3.19, the topology of this script consists of three routers and two hosts. You can notice that the three routers shown in the figure are arranged in a linear way. It is also worth noting that host h1 is connected to router r1, while host h2 is connected to the router r3.

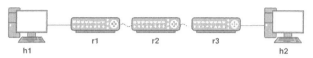

Figure 3.19: Dynamic routing topology.

Now, if we ping between h1 and h2, it will become evident that it is possible to establish communication between them.

```
mininet> h1 ping -c1 h2
PING 10.0.3.10 (10.0.3.10) 56(84) bytes of data.
64 bytes from 10.0.3.10: icmp_seq=1 ttl=61 time=0.093 ms

--- 10.0.3.10 ping statistics ---
1 packets transmitted, 1 received, 0% packet loss, time 0ms
rtt min/avg/max/mdev = 0.093/0.093/0.093/0.000 ms
```

This communication was only possible due to the RIP routing protocol (see *<rip.py>*), which was started together with *<routerline.py>*.

Unlike static routing, in dynamic routing the routing protocol configures all routing tables and also interacts with their routers, which have the same active routing protocol. Note that we basically got the nodes to communicate with each other effortlessly.

3.6.6 Firewall

Requirement(s): *iptables*

A firewall acts as a defense for a local computer or network against several threats, such as viruses, worms, trojans, and other malicious code. It can be software (a security program) or hardware (a physical router), but both have the same function: the analysis of incoming or outgoing network traffic to check for blacklisted data. Firewalls check each data packet (small pieces of a larger whole, reduced in size for easy transmission) to ensure that they do not contain anything malicious.

In this tutorial, we will use *iptables* and create a rule that will block communication between two nodes. *Iptables* is a firewall software that allows the administration of tables within the kernel of any Linux operating system. You do not need to have prior knowledge of the kernel, nor of the tables inside it, in order to modify the firewall and perform common system administration tasks. Usually, *iptables* is already installed on Linux systems.

 The Linux community recently announced *bpfilter*, a firewall that will surely replace *iptables*. It promises to improve performance as well as to ensure a smooth transition from *iptables* for Linux users.

Returning to the purpose of this tutorial, let us create our firewall rule by using Mininet-WiFi's simplest topology.

```
~/mininet-wifi$ sudo mn --wifi
```

Then, from the Mininet-WiFi CLI, let us create a single rule that does not allow sta2 to receive *echo request* messages.

```
mininet-wifi> sta2 iptables -A INPUT -p icmp --icmp-type echo-request -j
↪ DROP
```

Next, we can ping to confirm that sta2 does not actually respond to the *echo request* sent by sta1.

```
mininet-wifi> sta1 ping -c1 sta2
PING 10.0.0.2 (10.0.0.2) 56(84) bytes of data.

--- 10.0.0.2 ping statistics ---
1 packets transmitted, 0 received, 100% packet loss, time 0ms
```

Now, let us try the inverse, that is, an attempt to *ping* sta1 from sta2.

```
mininet-wifi> sta2 ping -c1 sta1
PING 10.0.0.1 (10.0.0.1) 56(84) bytes of data.
64 bytes from 10.0.0.1: icmp_seq=1 ttl=64 time=0.073 ms

--- 10.0.0.1 ping statistics ---
1 packets transmitted, 1 received, 0% packet loss, time 0ms
rtt min/avg/max/mdev = 0.073/0.073/0.073/0.000 ms
```

As we can see, `sta2` is able to communicate with `sta1` because only the *echo request* was blocked, which in the former case was done by `sta1`. In the latter case, the *echo request* was sent by `sta2` as an OUTPUT packet and not INPUT, as defined in the rule.

 If you had to block *ping* operations from `sta2` to `sta1`, what would you do? If you intend to use the *echo request* as an OUTPUT of `sta2`, or even as an INPUT to `sta1`, you were right. For example: `iptables -A OUTPUT -p icmp -icmp-type echo-request -j DROP`

In this case, no ICMP packets could be generated by `sta2`, since they would all be blocked.

Now, let us do an operation similar to the one done earlier but changing the protocol and setting a port number.

To do so, we will run *<internet.py>*.

```
~/mininet-wifi$ sudo python mn-wifi-book-en/codes/cap3/internet.py
```

With Mininet-WiFi running, we will try to make sure that google.com's port 80 is open. This is a simple test, and its answer is yes, google.com's port 80 is open, since it is a web page available on the internet.

The port verification test will be done using *telnet*, a network protocol that makes it possible to check ports and tell whether they are open or not, in addition to other functions.

```
mininet-wifi> sta1 telnet google.com 80
Trying 216.58.202.78...
Connected to google.com.
Escape character is '^]'.
^]^]
telnet> quit
Connection closed.
mininet-wifi>
```

If *telnet* does not work, and in turn a message appears stating that it was not possible to reach google.com, you will need to check whether a DNS server is properly configured on your system and if there are no active firewall rules preventing connection to port 80.

Hence, as a way of simulating an attempt to protect a fictitious internal network, we will block port 80 so that it cannot be reached.

 After starting a *telnet* session, you can exit it by pressing Ctrl+], exactly as indicated by the *"Escape character is ^]"* message. The ^ character means the Control key on the keyboard.

To do so, we will apply the following rule. It instructs the system that any outgoing packet corresponding to the TCP protocol that enters the sta1-wlan0 interface with the destination port 80 must be dropped.

```
mininet-wifi> sta1 iptables -A OUPUT -p tcp -i sta1-wlan0 --dport 80 -j
↪ DROP
```

Once the rule is applied, we can open a new telnet session on port 80 and confirm that it is possible to reach port 80.

```
mininet-wifi> sta1 telnet google.com 80
Trying 216.58.202.78...
```

After some time you will notice that you cannot communicate with google.com on port 80. Because port 80 is locked, sta1 will try to communicate with it indefinitely. In these cases, you can cancel the communication attempt by pressing "Ctrl + c".

You can also do blocking actions by checking IP addresses, and even block Internet pages with *iptables*, although the latter option is not so suitable to be carried out using firewalls, but rather through proxy servers.

3.6.7 Quality of Service (QoS)

 Requirement(s): *Ryu*

Quality of Service (QoS) allows you to define access priorities among flows - making video calls and online games, for example -, so that they have high priorities over any other type of traffic that can cross the network. QoS is especially useful in networks with many clients and, if well used, can significantly improve connection quality, reducing the need for a connection with greater transferability.

The purpose of this tutorial is to understand how OpenFlow rules can be defined in the context of QoS. Regarding the OpenFlow protocol, these rules are treated as *meter tables*. To start this tutorial, use *<qos.py>*, which is a relatively simple file, since it has only one station, one access point, and one host, as shown in Figure 3.20. Rules added to the access point will instruct it to limit the bandwidth that passes through it to up to 5 Mbits/s.

Before issuing this tutorial's script, you need to open a terminal and run *Ryu*.

```
~/mininet-wifi/ryu$ sudo PYTHONPATH=. ./bin/ryu-manager
↪ ryu/app/simple_switch_13.py
```

Then, on a new terminal, execute *<qos.py>*, as follows:

```
~/mininet-wifi$ sudo python mn-wifi-book-en/codes/cap3/qos.py
```

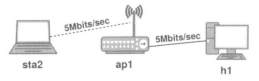

Figure 3.20: QoS topology.

Then measure the bandwidth between h1 and sta1 with *iperf*. Do this on two terminals using *xterm*. Note that h1 is the server and sta1 the client. Unlike earlier tutorials, here we will use 10 Mb UDP packets (-u parameter).

```
mininet-wifi> xterm h1 sta1

h1# iperf -s -u
------------------------------------------------------------
Server listening on UDP port 5001
Receiving 1470 byte datagrams
UDP buffer size:  208 KByte (default)
------------------------------------------------------------
[ 15] local 10.0.0.2 port 5001 connected with 10.0.0.1 port 49733
[ ID] Interval       Transfer     Bandwidth        Jitter   Lost/Total
↪  Datagrams
[ 15]  0.0-10.8 sec  12.5 MBytes  9.68 Mbits/sec   0.095 ms    0/ 8918 (0%)

sta1# iperf -c 10.0.0.2 -u -b 10M
------------------------------------------------------------
Client connecting to 10.0.0.2, UDP port 5001
Sending 1470 byte datagrams, IPG target: 1121.52 us (kalman adjust)
UDP buffer size:  208 KByte (default)
------------------------------------------------------------
[ 15] local 10.0.0.1 port 49733 connected with 10.0.0.2 port 5001
[ ID] Interval       Transfer     Bandwidth
[ 15]  0.0-10.0 sec  12.5 MBytes  10.5 Mbits/sec
```

Note that the client transferred data with a bandwidth close to 10 Mbits/s, and the server also received data at a rate of around 10 Mbits/s. In other words, here it can be seen that the server was able to receive approximately the same amount of data sent by sta1.

Now, we will close Mininet-WiFi, and run it again with the -q parameter, as demonstrated below.

```
mininet-wifi> exit
~/mininet-wifi$ sudo python mn-wifi-book-en/codes/cap3/qos.py -q
```

Then, run *iperf* again, exactly as was done earlier.

```
h1# iperf -s -u
------------------------------------------------------------
Server listening on UDP port 5001
Receiving 1470 byte datagrams
UDP buffer size:  208 KByte (default)
------------------------------------------------------------
[ 15] local 10.0.0.2 port 5001 connected with 10.0.0.1 port 47218
[ ID] Interval       Transfer     Bandwidth        Jitter   Lost/Total
↪  Datagrams
[ 15]  0.0-10.8 sec  5.72 MBytes  4.43 Mbits/sec   0.293 ms  4835/ 8917
↪  (54%)
```

```
sta1# iperf -c 10.0.0.2 -u -b 10M
-----------------------------------------------------------------
Client connecting to 10.0.0.2, UDP port 5001
Sending 1470 byte datagrams, IPG target: 1121.52 us (kalman adjust)
UDP buffer size:  208 KByte (default)
-----------------------------------------------------------------
[ 15] local 10.0.0.1 port 47218 connected with 10.0.0.2 port 5001
[ ID] Interval        Transfer      Bandwidth
[ 15]  0.0-10.0 sec  12.5 MBytes  10.5 Mbits/sec
```

We can see that the client again transferred data at a rate of about 10 Mbit/s. However, this time, the server was limited to responding up to 5 Mbits/s. Or, more precisely, 4.43 Mbits/s. This was due to the OpenFlow rules that were defined for access point ap1, which are included in the script we just ran.

 It is important to note that this tutorial used OVSAP as the access point. However, OVS does not support *meter tables* without *datapath* being set as *user* (see script). This is due to OVS's limitations.

Although in this tutorial we used a simple rule to limit bandwidth, rules can be customized in order to impose different bandwidth values for different types of traffic, as well as to impose different traffic profile priorities.

3.6.8 MultiPath TCP (MP-TCP)

 Requirement(s): *MP-TCP*

MultiPath TCP (MP-TCP) is a set of extensions to the TCP protocol that enables reliable transmission over multiple end-to-end paths between client and server in computer networks, especially on the Internet. Two benefits are immediately obtained with the use of MP-TCP: the increase in end-to-end throughput via the aggregation of multiple TCP sub-flows; and greater tolerance to communication failure, since should a sub-flow become unavailable, one or more sub-flows will remain active.

The use of MP-TCP usually requires its installation, and afterwards it is necessary to use the kernel that will be created during the installation process. The installation process is simple and can be done by running *apt*.

```
~/mininet-wifi$ sudo apt install linux-mptcp
```

```
GNU GRUB  version 2.02~beta2-29ubuntu0.3

Ubuntu, with Linux 4.2.0-42-generic
Ubuntu, with Linux 4.2.0-42-generic (recovery mode)
Ubuntu, with Linux 4.2.0-38-generic
Ubuntu, with Linux 4.2.0-38-generic (recovery mode)
Ubuntu, with Linux 4.2.0-35-generic
Ubuntu, with Linux 4.2.0-35-generic (recovery mode)
Ubuntu, with Linux 4.2.0-30-generic
Ubuntu, with Linux 4.2.0-30-generic (recovery mode)
Ubuntu, with Linux 4.1.35.mptcp
Ubuntu, with Linux 4.1.35.mptcp (recovery mode)
```

Figure 3.21: MP-TCP Kernel.

If you cannot install it using *apt*, you can find up-to-date information on how to install MP-TCP on its official website[6].

Since there is a kernel that is loaded by default when you start the operating system, you will need to choose the MP-TCP kernel before the operating system starts booting. A screen similar to Figure 3.21 should be displayed. You can easily identify the MP-TCP kernel, since there is a kernel with such name.

With MP-TCP installed and selected during the system boot, let us execute the tutorial script, *<mptcp.py>*. We recommend that you check its contents before doing so, however, as they contain the whole MP-TCP configuration code.

 You may need to issue the *uname -a* command on the terminal to make sure that the kernel created for MP-TCP is being used.

After checking the contents of the script, run it:

```
~/mininet-wifi$ sudo python mn-wifi-book-en/codes/cap3/mptcp.py -m
```

Now open two terminals by running *xterm* from the Mininet-WiFi CLI.

---

[6]multipath-tcp.org/

```
mininet-wifi> xterm sta1 h1
```

Then, using *iperf*, make it so that h1 and sta1 operate as client and server, respectively. The throughput test will yield a similar result to the one shown below.

```
sta1# iperf -s
------------------------------------------------------------
Server listening on TCP port 5001
TCP window size: 85.3 KByte (default)
------------------------------------------------------------
[ 20] local 10.0.0.2 port 5001 connected with 10.0.2.2 port 38248
[ ID] Interval      Transfer     Bandwidth
[ 20]  0.0-10.1 sec   227 MBytes   188 Mbits/sec

h1# iperf -c 10.0.0.2
------------------------------------------------------------
Client connecting to 10.0.0.2, TCP port 5001
TCP window size: 86.2 KByte (default)
------------------------------------------------------------
[ 19] local 10.0.2.2 port 38268 connected with 10.0.0.2 port 5001
[ ID] Interval      Transfer     Bandwidth
[ 19]  0.0-10.0 sec   228 MBytes   191 Mbits/sec
```

Now, close Mininet-WiFi and try running the same script - <*mptcp.py*> - without adding -*m*, as follows.

```
mininet-wifi> exit
~/mininet-wifi$ sudo python mn-wifi-book-en/codes/cap3/mptcp.py
```

This script without -*m* is programmed to disassociate sta1 from ap2. Thus, since ap2 was operating on IEEE 802.11n and was therefore responsible for providing most of the throughput obtained in the previous test (about 190 Mbits/s), the resulting throughput in this new test will most likely be significantly lower than that of the previous one.

We can confirm this hypothesis, as demonstrated below.

```
sta1# iperf -s
------------------------------------------------------------
Server listening on TCP port 5001
TCP window size: 85.3 KByte (default)
------------------------------------------------------------
[ 20] local 10.0.0.2 port 5001 connected with 10.0.2.2 port 38404
[ ID] Interval      Transfer     Bandwidth
[ 20]  0.0-10.5 sec   63.6 MBytes   50.9 Mbits/sec
```

```
h1# iperf -c 10.0.0.2
-----------------------------------------------------------
Client connecting to 10.0.0.2, TCP port 5001
TCP window size: 86.2 KByte (default)
-----------------------------------------------------------
[ 19] local 10.0.2.2 port 38378 connected with 10.0.0.2 port 5001
[ ID] Interval       Transfer     Bandwidth
[ 19]  0.0-10.1 sec  63.1 MBytes  52.6 Mbits/sec
```

As you can see, the throughput has indeed dropped a lot - to around 50 Mbits/s.

Studies that previously used Mininet-WiFi for research on MP-TCP:

- Qi Zhao, Muhao Chen, Pengyuan Du, Tuan Le, Mario Gerla, *Towards Efficient Cellular Traffic Offloading via Dynamic MPTCP Path Configuration with SDN.* (ICNC'19), Honolulu, Hawaii, USA, February 2019.
- Singh, Pranav Kumar et al. *Multipath TCP for V2I communication in SDN controlled small cell deployment of smart city.* Vehicular communications. 2019.
- Zhao, Qi et al. *Software Defined Multi-Path TCP Solution for Mobile Wireless Tactical Networks.* In: MILCOM. IEEE. 2018.

Level: expert

4. Expert

In this chapter, we will explore the main experiments with wireless networks that we have developed using Mininet-WiFi. As described earlier in this book, this chapter is labeled as Expert because it requires more in-depth knowledge and/or use of third-party applications.

4.1 Manipulating kernel modules

In this tutorial, we will understand how operating system modules can be modified and how it is possible to contribute to the development of the Linux kernel. As an example, we will modify the main operating module of Mininet-WiFi, mac80211_hwsim. This module is included in the source code of the Linux kernel and can be found at https://github.com/torvalds/linux/blob/master/drivers/net/wireless/mac80211_hwsim.c.

First of all, we need to create a *"Makefile"*, which is how the file responsible for setting compilation rules for Linux systems is called. In this tutorial, this file will compile the module to be modified. To generate the *Makefile*, let us first create a new directory named *<myModule>*. If you do not know how to create directories using the CLI, the following command will do so.

```
~/mininet-wifi$ sudo mkdir myModule
~/mininet-wifi$ cd myModule
~/mininet-wifi/myModule$
```

Then, within the *<myModule>* directory, create the *Makefile* with the following content using your favorite text editor.

```
obj-m += mac80211_hwsim.o

all:
        make -C /lib/modules/$(shell uname -r)/build M=$(PWD) modules

clean:
        make -C /lib/modules/$(shell uname -r)/build M=$(PWD) clean
```

 The lines shown above have to be indented by tabs, otherwise the *Makefile* will not work as expected.

After that, you need to identify the kernel version of the Linux operating system you are using and then copy the module from the Github page, which we will modify.

```
$ uname -a
Linux alpha-Inspiron 4.15.0-15-generic #16~16.04.1-Ubuntu SMP
Thu Apr 5 12:19:23 UTC 2018 x86_64 x86_64 x86_64 GNU/Linux
```

According to the output of the command issued above, the kernel version is 4.15. Execute the same command to check your own kernel version. Then visit the mac80211_hwsim[1] module web page and select your kernel version from the *branch* menu. Then copy the contents of the module and save them to a file inside the *<myModule>* directory with the same module name. Repeat the same procedure for mac80211_hwsim.h[2].

Once you have finished all the steps so far, the contents of the *<myModule>* directory will be exactly the same as those shown by the *ls* command.

---

[1] https://github.com/torvalds/linux/blob/master/drivers/net/wireless/mac80211_hwsim.c

[2] https://github.com/torvalds/linux/blob/master/drivers/net/wireless/mac80211_hwsim.h

```
~/myModule$ ls
Makefile mac80211_hwsim.c mac80211_hwsim.h
```

Now, let us compile the *mac80211_hwsim* module. If all goes well, an output similar to the text shown below should appear.

```
~/mininet-wifi/myModule$ make
make -C /lib/modules/4.15.0-15-generic/build
 ↪  M=/home/alpha/mininet-wifi/myModule modules
make[1]: Entering directory '/usr/src/linux-headers-4.15.0-15-generic'
  CC [M]  /home/alpha/mininet-wifi/myModule/mac80211_hwsim.o
  Building modules, stage 2.
  MODPOST 1 modules
  CC      /home/alpha/mininet-wifi/myModule/mac80211_hwsim.mod.o
  LD [M]  /home/alpha/mininet-wifi/myModule/mac80211_hwsim.ko
make[1]: Leaving directory '/usr/src/linux-headers-4.15.0-15-generic'
```

Then double-check the contents of the *<myModule>* directory. Now, something similar to the content below should be noted.

```
~/myModule$ ls
mac80211_hwsim.h      mac80211_hwsim.mod.o      Makefile
mac80211_hwsim.ko     mac80211_hwsim.o          modules.order
mac80211_hwsim.mod.c  Module.symvers
```

At this point, you should already have your version of the mac80211_hwsim module compiled and, in addition to being able to use it, you can also modify and recompile it for later use in Mininet-WiFi. For instance, run *<my-module.py>*. This script includes a call to the new module.

```
~/mininet-wifi$ sudo python myModule/my-module.py
```

Then observe the signal strength perceived by sta1.

```
mininet-wifi> sta1 iw dev sta1-wlan0 link
Connected to 02:00:00:00:01:00 (on sta1-wlan0)
        SSID: new-ssid
        freq: 2412
        RX: 7978 bytes (155 packets)
        TX: 806 bytes (9 packets)
        signal: -36 dBm
        tx bitrate: 1.0 MBit/s

        bss flags:      short-slot-time
        dtim period:    2
        beacon int:     100
```

Without *Wmediumd*, which has been described previously in the book, signal strength is calculated by mac80211_hwsim through a simple formula, which subtracts 50 from the *txpower* value, which in this case is 14 dBm, resulting in the value of -36 dBm obtained previously.

So let us modify the module so that it returns another value. For example, if Mininet-WiFi is running, shut it down, look for the text *rx_status.signal = -50* in the contents of the mac80211_hwsim.c file, and replace -50 by -40. Then recompile the module using the *make* command.

Finally, run the *<my-module.py>* script one more time.

```
~/mininet-wifi$ sudo python myModule/my-module.py
```

Now rerun *iw* to check the signal strength perceived by sta1.

```
mininet-wifi> sta1 iw dev sta1-wlan0 link
Connected to 02:00:00:00:01:00 (on sta1-wlan0)
        SSID: new-ssid
        freq: 2412
        RX: 968 bytes (17 packets)
        TX: 310 bytes (4 packets)
        signal: -26 dBm
        tx bitrate: 1.0 MBit/s

        bss flags:        short-slot-time
        dtim period:      2
        beacon int:       100
```

As expected, after changing the formula for calculating the received signal level, the signal value also has changed.

Once you understand how the mac80211_hwsim module works, you can make any modifications and extend it as needed. You can also submit improvements to the discussion group about the Linux kernel, more specifically the group discussing aspects of the IEEE 802.11 protocol[3].

It is worth mentioning that the mac80211_hwsim module is based on mac80211, a framework used by wireless device driver developers. Therefore, any extensions for mac80211_hwsim must be previously supported by mac80211.

---

[3]https://wireless.wiki.kernel.org/

4.2 Traffic monitoring with sFlow-RT

  Requirement(s): *sFlow-RT*

Monitoring network traffic is an important step in avoiding problems and keeping services always ready to respond when needed. Proper network management enables a better use of information technology resources, delivering the expected return on technology investments undertaken by a company.

Other advantages of network management over network traffic monitoring include: system failure detection; as a result of this detection, quicker and more efficient error fixing; identification of traffic patterns, including peak demand periods; performance visualization; among other features.

In the context of software-defined networks, *sFlow-RT*, a program that provides real-time monitoring capability, has proven to be a very interesting tool for processing *sFlow* packets received by a given network. By acting on the SDN stack control plane, sFlow-RT changes the received datagrams into summary statistics or actionable metrics in flows, as chosen by the user. A set of packets with a common property constitutes a traffic stream known as a stream key, which is observed within a time interval.

As you may expect, in this tutorial we will learn to monitor wireless traffic using *sFlow-RT*. To do so, we will need to copy *sFlow-RT*'s source code, which is available on its official website[4]. There, you should see several packages that were developed for *sFlow-RT*. Of those packages, we will need to install the one called *mininet-dashboard.*

 sFlow (Sampled Flow) is an industry standard for exporting packets on the second layer (layer 2) of the OSI model. It provides a means to do so with interface counters for network monitoring purposes. Its maintenance is done by the sFlow.org consortium.

Then, assuming that the *sFlow-RT* source code and the *mininet-dashboard*

---

[4]https://sflow-rt.com/

package have already been copied, we will start *sFlow-RT* by executing the command below.

```
~$ cd sflow-rt
~/sflow-rt$ ./start.sh
```

After starting it, you should be able to open the *mininet-dashboard*[5] package, with which you can monitor flows in real time. However, you will still need to create the flows in order to view them using *sFlow-RT*. To create them, let us start a script that includes some instructions on how to make *sFlow-RT* interpret or recognize the wireless interfaces created for the wireless nodes on Mininet-WiFi.

```
~/mininet-wifi$ sudo python mn-wifi-book-en/codes/cap4/sflow-rt.py
```

 If for some reason you cannot execute <*sflow-rt.py*>, and instead a message appears stating that a package was not found, then you must install it first.

Next, let us open one terminal for sta1, another for sta2, and then generate some data traffic between them via *iperf*.

```
mininet-wifi> xterm sta1 sta2
```

Note that the sta1 node was chosen to be the server and sta2 the client.

```
sta1# iperf -s
```

```
sta2# iperf -c 10.0.0.1 -t 100
```

Finally, after starting *iperf*, you can already see real-time flows with *sFlow-RT*, as shown in Figure 4.1. Note, also, that in addition to allowing you to observe data traffic in real time, *sFlow-RT* can display the topology of the network on its topology tab.

  Integration between Mininet-WiFi and sflow-rt:
https://youtu.be/4ccua2b26k8

---

[5]http://127.0.0.1:8008/app/mininet-dashboard/html/

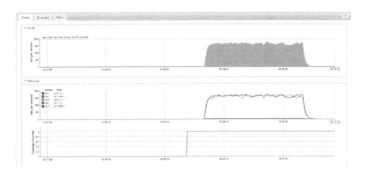

Figure 4.1: sFlow-RT.

4.3 Reproducing network behavior

There are situations in which it is necessary to reproduce real network traffic conditions based on traffic observations from real environments, allowing fair comparisons between the physical and virtual environments to be done. Reproducing network traffic behavior is one of Mininet-WiFi's features. Below, we will learn about two types of network traffic behavior reproduction: network attributes and mobility.

4.3.1 Network attributes

The first parameter of behavioral reproduction that we will use is called network attributes, by which link parameters, such as bandwidth, packet loss, latency and delay, can be dynamically configured. As a result, we will eventually be able to notice the proximity of the values collected from real-world experiments in relation to those obtained in a virtual way by using Mininet-WiFi.

For instance, imagine that at any given moment there is a network that displays a certain behavior pattern and you need to reproduce it on Mininet-WiFi. Imagine also that your task is to perform overload tests or any other test that demands the simulation of the network at that moment. This is exactly what we propose in this tutorial.

To accomplish this, we will use a capture file that will serve as a basis for the demonstration of bandwidth variation and latency. With the capture data already saved in a text file, all we need to do is run a Mininet-WiFi script that will*Play* the traces recorded in the text file. Let us use *<replayingNetworkConditions.py>* as an example.

```
~/mininet-wifi$ sudo python
↳  mn-wifi-book-en/codes/cap4/replayingNetworkConditions.py
```

 Bandwidth traces can be acquired using *iperf*, and latency can be seen by issuing a *ping*.

Then, by using the Mininet-WiFi CLI and TC, we can observe the bandwidth variation of sta1's sta1-wlan0 interface. *The following output has been filtered to display only the data that interests us.*

```
mininet-wifi> sta1 tc qdisc
qdisc netem 2: dev sta1-wlan0 root refcnt 5 limit 1000 rate 1567Kbit
mininet-wifi> sta1 tc qdisc
qdisc netem 2: dev sta1-wlan0 root refcnt 5 limit 1000 rate 1669Kbit
mininet-wifi> sta1 tc qdisc
qdisc netem 2: dev sta1-wlan0 root refcnt 5 limit 1000 rate 1513Kbit
```

Our previous use of TC served only to demonstrate that, in fact, traces are being reproduced in Mininet-WiFi. Alternatively, the most varied network applications can be used for more specific tests while the network reproducibility feature is running. E.g. it would be possible to use *iperf* itself to measure the bandwidth and *ping* to observe the latency.

4.3.2 Mobility

Another way to reproduce network behavior in Mininet-WiFi is by reproducing mobility. To reproduce the mobility of nodes in a real environment, it is necessary to define the x and y coordinates, and optionally z when altitude is required. These coordinates can be obtained from any source, such as equipment with GPS support.

In this tutorial, we will use *<replayingMobility.py>* and a text file that already has the data needed for reproducibility purposes, just as we did in 4.3.1.

```
~/mininet-wifi$ sudo python mn-wifi-book-en/codes/cap4/replayingMobility.py
```

Once the script is executed, we can perceive the mobility of a given node by viewing the information contained in the position parameter, as follows:

```
mininet-wifi> py sta1.position
(24.0, 15.0, 0.0)
mininet-wifi> py sta1.position
(29.0, 20.0, 0.0)
mininet-wifi> py sta1.position
(34.0, 25.0, 0.0)
mininet-wifi> py sta1.position
(37.0, 28.0, 0.0)
mininet-wifi> py sta1.position
(42.0, 33.0, 0.0)
```

While sta1 is moving around, you can use *iw* to check associations and observe variations in latency and bandwidth. Other tools such as *ping* or *iperf*, can be used for the same purpose, with the former monitoring latency and the latter bandwidth.

4.4 Socket - low-level networking interface

You can access the network interfaces of Mininet-WiFi's nodes in basically three ways:

- Python API (e.g. sta1.cmd() or sta1.pexec())
- Mininet-WiFi CLI or an xterm
- util/m (e.g. m sta1 ifconfig)

However, there may be times when you will need to access nodes from outside Mininet-WiFi. Moreover, you might need to access node attributes that were implemented on the Mininet-WiFi code base, such as *node.setPosition()*. To do so, you can use Python's socket module.

The socket module provides access to the BSD socket interface. It is available on all modern Unix systems, Windows, MacOS, and probably on additional platforms as well. In this tutorial, you will learn to start a socket server and client using Python and set the position for a node from outside Mininet-WiFi

CLI.

First, you need to execute the socket server code as follows:

```
~/mininet-wifi$ sudo python mn-wifi-book-en/codes/cap3/socket-server.py
```

The topology of this code consists of two stations, one access point and one host. Now, you need to open a new terminal and run the socket client code.

```
~/mininet-wifi$ sudo python mn-wifi-book-en/codes/cap3/socket-client.py
```

Then you should be able to see the following symbol on the terminal:

```
->
```

And after setting the position, in addition to receiving a response from the server saying that the command was accepted, you will be able to observe, on the graph, the new position defined for the node.

```
set.sta1.setPosition.40,40,40
Received from server: command accepted!
```

This feature is very important and can be used in many research projects, such as those involving the use of GPS (e.g. to develop self-driving cars).

4.5   P4

P4 (Programming Protocol-Independent Packet Processors)[6] is a recent domain-specific language for programming network data plane pipelines. It is an open source programming language that allows users to dictate how networking hardware should operate. It can be used to (re-)define the pipeline of silicon processor chips in network forwarding devices, such as switches, routers and network interface cards.

The purpose of P4 is to describe the behavior of the data plane pipeline of any system or appliance that forwards, modifies or inspects network traffic. Research on the design and implementation of networked systems built using

---

[6]https://p4.org

P4 has been growing significantly. P4 publications[7] touch multiple topics, including innovating by using P4 in server-based networking systems to offload data plane functions to SmartNICs and hardware switches supporting P4.

To this day, a number of shy, small-scale studies on the use of P4 in wireless networks have been developed. Still, this combination promises to enable the creation of truly flexible networks, to provide several advantages to NFV, improve HW performance, among other benefits.

4.5.1   Differences between P4 and OpenFlow

You may have probably heard that P4 is commonly regarded as the 2.0 version of the OpenFlow protocol. However, it is NOT OpenFlow 2.0, as some have mooted. Although they are both focused on opening up the forwarding plane, P4 addresses a different need in the network data plane: deep programmability, from arbitrary packet header parsing through a pipeline of match and action tables to the deparsing.

Once a P4 program is compiled to invoke a target datapath, P4Runtime APIs[8] are used to manage the entries of the tables and to send/receive packets to/from the control plane, which can be local (traditional distributed models) or remote (SDN controller).

After this brief introduction to P4, let us see how it works in practice. To do so, we will run three scenarios: a basic WiFi scenario; a handover scenario; and a scenario of dropping packets based on BSSID. In order to run these three scenarios, you need to copy the source code available at https://github.com/ramonfontes/tutorials.

> ~/mininet-wifi$ git clone https://github.com/ramonfontes/tutorials

 This tutorial does not cover P4's installation process. You can either download the P4 VM available on the Internet or install it on your host.

---

[7]https://p4.org/publications/
[8]https://p4.org/p4-runtime/

4.5.2 Basic WiFi scenario

The goal of this tutorial is to write a P4 program that implements basic forwarding. To keep things simple, we will implement forwarding only for IPv4. With IPv4 forwarding, the switch must perform the following actions for every packet that crosses it: (i) update the source and destination MAC addresses; (ii) decrement the Time-To-Live (TTL) in the IP header; and (iii) forward the packet out through the appropriate port.

The access points will have a single table, which the control plane will populate with static rules. Each rule will map an IP address to the MAC address and output port for the next hop. We have already defined the control plane rules, so you only need to implement the data plane logic of your P4 program.

The topology used in this tutorial (Figure 4.2) consists of four stations and four access points. While stations sta1 and sta2 are associated with access point ap1, stations sta3 and sta4 are associated with access point ap2.

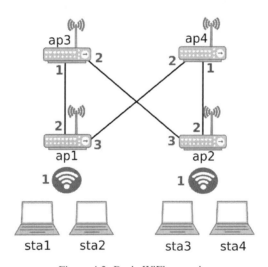

Figure 4.2: Basic WiFi scenario.

Since our P4 program is already included in the *<solution/basic.p4>* file, we will use it in our scenario. With that said, you need to copy *<solution/basic.p4>*

to the *<basic-wifi>* directory, as follows.

```
~/mininet-wifi/tutorials/exercises$ cd basic-wifi
~/mininet-wifi/tutorials/exercises/basic-wifi$ cp solution/basic.p4 .
```

Then, you can compile the script by issuing the *make* command.

```
~/mininet-wifi/tutorials/exercises/basic-wifi$ sudo make
```

Mininet-WiFi should be running right now, and you can use the CLI to confirm that all nodes can communicate with each other.

In addition to *<basic.p4>*, other relevant files are included in the set of *JSON* files located in the *<pod-top>* directory. There you can find important information, such as tables with matches and actions that populate switches and access points.

4.5.3 Handover

The goal of this tutorial is to write a P4 program that implements a basic protocol for WiFi in order to provide seamless handover. With this basic protocol active, switch s3 must perform the following action: forward packets from sta1 to h2.

As illustrated in Figure 4.3, the topology used in this tutorial consists of one station, two access points, one switch and two hosts (one of which functions as controller).

Before running the tutorial script, let us understand the process we will reproduce. First, sta1 is associated with ap1 and moves towards ap2. While it is roaming to ap2, ICMP packets are being sent to h2. Access point ap1, in turn, sends its BSSID and the MAC address of all stations associated with it to h3, which is the controller. While sta1 is associated with ap1, an instruction in s3 says that to reach sta1, the ICMP reply must be sent through its number three port. However, when sta1 performs the handover to ap2, s3 should learn about (or be aware of) the handover. The tutorial code will do just that, update the existing table in s3.

Let us see this in practice. To do so, you should copy the *<basic.p4>* file to the handover directory, as follows.

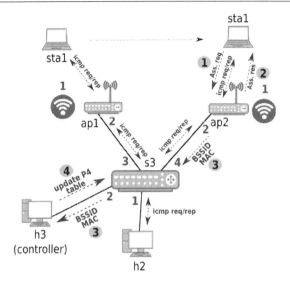

Figure 4.3: Handover scenario.

```
~/mininet-wifi/tutorials/exercises$ cd handover
~/mininet-wifi/tutorials/exercises/handover$ cp solution/basic.p4 .
```

Now, you can compile the script using the *make* command.

```
~/mininet-wifi/tutorials/exercises/handover$ sudo make
```

Mininet-WiFi should be running now, and you will be able to see sta1 moving towards ap2 while ICMP packets are being sent to h2. In the end, only one or two ICMP packets will be lost after sta1 does the handover to h2.

So, how did the communication between sta1 and h2 remain uninterrupted? When ap2 (1) receives the association request, it responds with an (2) association response message to sta1 and (3) sends a custom packet with its BSSID and the MAC address of sta1 to h3. After receiving this packet, h3 (4) installs new tables in s3 using a new JSON located in <*topo-handover/s3-runtime.json*>.

Of course, updating an entire switch table may not be - and often is not -

ideal. Therefore, we recommend that you create your own programming logic
in your p4 file.

 In the *<receive.py>* file you can find a call to *<run-code.sh>*,
which has a command you can use to update the table in s3.

 P4+Mininet-WiFi: Handover scenario:
`https://www.youtube.com/watch?v=v-_gQ7I4RXc`

4.5.4 Dropping packets based on BSSID

The goal of this tutorial is to write a P4 program that implements a basic protocol for WiFi. With this basic protocol, switch s3 must perform the following
action: drop any packet created by ap2.

The topology used in this tutorial (Figure 4.4) consists of two stations, two
access points, one switch and one host. Associated with ap1, sta1 should be
able to communicate with h3. On the other hand, sta2 should not be able to
communicate with h3 due to the BSSID issued by ap2. In a hypothetical case,
only allowed BSSIDs can have network access.

As was done earlier, you need to copy *<solution/basic.p4>* to the *<bssid-
based>* directory, as follows.

```
~/mininet-wifi/tutorials/exercises$ cd bssid-based
~/mininet-wifi/tutorials/exercises/bssid-based$ cp solution/basic.p4 .
```

Now, you can compile the script by running the *make* command.

```
~/mininet-wifi/tutorials/exercises/bssid-based$ sudo make
```

Mininet-WiFi should be running now, and you can see three terminals: one
showing ap1 sending an amount of data to h4; another one showing ap2 sending data to h4; and a final one showing packets received by h4, the controller.

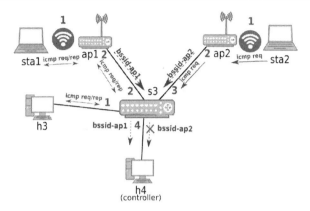

Figure 4.4: BSSID based scenario.

At first, `sta2` is out of range in relation to all access points, including ap2. Thus, you must move `sta2` towards ap2.

```
mininet-wifi> py sta2.setPosition('500,200,0')
```

Now, ap2 should send a packet to h4 that contains its BSSID, and h4 should update the table installed in s3. This update will make s3 drop packets directed to ap2.

```
mininet-wifi> py sta2.setPosition('500,200,0')
```

Now, try a *ping* between `sta2` and h3 to confirm the new rules.

```
mininet-wifi> sta2 ping -c1 10.0.3.3
PING 10.0.3.3 (10.0.3.3) 56(84) bytes of data.

--- 10.0.3.3 ping statistics ---
1 packets transmitted, 0 received, 100% packet loss, time 0ms
```

As we can see, `sta2` cannot ping h3. Now, move `sta2` towards ap1.

```
mininet-wifi> py sta2.setPosition('100,200,0')
```

And try a new *ping* between `sta2` and h3.

```
mininet-wifi> sta2 ping -c1 10.0.3.3
PING 10.0.3.3 (10.0.3.3) 56(84) bytes of data.
64 bytes from 10.0.3.3: icmp_seq=1 ttl=62 time=70.3 ms

--- 10.0.3.3 ping statistics ---
1 packets transmitted, 1 received, 0% packet loss, time 0ms
rtt min/avg/max/mdev = 70.364/70.364/70.364/0.000 ms
```

As we can see, `sta2` is able to ping h3, since ap1's BSSID is allowed by the controller. In any case, `sta1` should be able to ping h3.

As mentioned before, updating an entire switch table may not be ideal. Therefore, you should create your own programming logic in your p4 file, instead of replacing the switch table.

 The logic implemented for the controller can be found in the *<receive.py>* file.

4.6   Use case scenarios

Next, we will do some tutorials involving slightly more advanced scenarios about computer networking in which Mininet-WiFi can be used.

4.6.1   Containers

 Requirement(s): *Docker*

Containers are lightweight execution environments similar to virtual machines that allow you to segregate processes so that they can be run independently. We can say that containers are instances of an image running at a given moment, by which different services can be segregated between different instances.

Among container-related technologies, *Docker* is certainly the most well-known and used container management program. *Docker* is an open source project written in *Go* that enables the packaging of an entire application or environment within a container, making the stored content portable to any other computer that has *Docker* installed.

A docker container image is a standalone, executable software package that includes everything needed to run a program: code, runtime, system tools, system libraries, and configurations.

Container images become containers during runtime, and in the case of *Docker* containers, the images become containers when they are executed using the *Docker Engine*. Given their compatibility with Linux and Windows-based operating systems, containerized software will always run the same way regardless of the system infrastructure. This impressive feature is possible due the containers' ability to isolate the software from its environment and ensure that it works in a uniform way, despite any differences, for instance, between its development and preparation.

Once we get to know a little more about containers and, most importantly, *Docker*, we will see in practice how their process works. We will consider, in the remainder of this section, *Docker* to be already installed.

Then, once you install *Docker* and get it up and running, execute the following command.

```
sudo docker run --privileged=true -it --env="DISPLAY"
↪ --env="QT_X11_NO_MITSHM=1" -v /tmp/.X11-unix:/tmp/.X11-unix:rw -v
↪ /sys/:/sys -v /lib/modules/:/lib/modules/ --name mininet-wifi
↪ --hostname mininet-wifi ramonfontes/mininet-wifi:latest /bin/bash
```

In general terms, the above command causes the container processes to become interactive, then it forwards the DISPLAY environment variable, mounts a volume in the unix X11 socket and registers the container ID. It also creates a container called Mininet-WiFi, so you will not be able to issue the same command twice or more, since the system does not allow the creation of two or more containers with the same name. On the other hand, you can remove containers using the *sudo docker rm* command or even create new containers with different names by adding the (*–name*) line.

Now, you can issue the command written below from inside the container. It will start Mininet-WiFi within the container (you will need to replace *username* with the username of your operating system).

```
root@mininet-wifi:/# sudo mn --wifi --docker --container mininet-wifi
↪ --ssh-user username
```

 Explaining the command: *--docker* enables Mininet-WiFi for use on Docker; *--container* indicates the name of the container; and *--ssh-user* indicates the username of the host. An SSH connection is required because some commands need to be run on the host in order to make Mininet-WiFi work properly.

Right now, you already have Mininet-WiFi running on one container, and you are able to create multiple containers. Additionally, multiple instances of Mininet-WiFi can also be started, one for each container. Different instances of Mininet-WiFi can be useful in situations where the integration of different types of environments, such as those characterized by different propagation models, is necessary.

4.6.2 Interaction between virtual and real environments

Now, we will learn about two ways by which virtual environments can interact with the real world: the first one involves the communication and interaction of nodes emulated by Mininet-Wifi with the Internet. The second one uses an additional wireless network card that can be connected to your computer.

Internet

 Requirement(s): script(s) only

Establishing communication between the virtual nodes and the Internet is possible and consists of a fairly simple task. In this tutorial, we will provide important information about the IP addressing step of this process and also about the default gateway's role in it.

First, let us understand what the default gateway is and how important it is to the network. To do so, run the following script.

```
~/mininet-wifi$ sudo python mn-wifi-book-en/codes/cap4/defaultgw.py
```

If we look at the topology configured in the script, we will see that it comprises an access point called r1 that is running from a station. What does that mean? It means that there is a station whose (two) wireless interfaces are operating in master mode, which is the mode of operation for interfaces acting as access points.

This topology also includes two other stations, whose interfaces are operating in managed mode, i.e. the mode of operation for clients. The sta1 station is associated with one of r1's interfaces, while sta2 is associated with another one.

After this brief explanation, try to *ping* between sta1 and sta2.

```
mininet-wifi> sta1 ping -c1 sta2
connect: Network is unreachable
```

 Why is sta1 not able to communicate with sta2? Try to answer that question before resuming your reading of this section.

As you can see, sta1 cannot communicate with sta2 and vice versa. Consequently, the message *Network is unreachable* is displayed. But what does it mean? To answer this question, let us first check whether both nodes, sta1 and sta2, are associated with the wireless router r1. If they are, this eliminates the possibility of the communication failure being related to the data link layer - in other words, to the absence of connectivity between sta1 and sta2.

```
mininet-wifi> sta1 iw dev sta1-wlan0 link
Connected to 02:00:00:00:02:00 (on sta1-wlan0)
        SSID: r1-ssid1
        freq: 2412
        RX: 2910 bytes (60 packets)
        TX: 718 bytes (8 packets)
        signal: -36 dBm
        tx bitrate: 11.0 MBit/s

        bss flags:      short-slot-time
        dtim period:    2
        beacon int:     100

mininet-wifi> sta2 iw dev sta2-wlan0 link
Connected to 02:00:00:00:03:00 (on sta2-wlan0)
```

```
SSID: r1-ssid2
freq: 2412
RX: 6078 bytes (130 packets)
TX: 806 bytes (9 packets)
signal: -36 dBm
tx bitrate: 9.0 MBit/s

bss flags:          short-slot-time
dtim period:        2
beacon int:         100
```

This association indicates that the communication failure is not related to problems in the interaction of sta1 and sta2 with r1, since they appear to remain associated with r1. Thus, we will keep trying to identify the reason for the lack of communication between sta1 and sta2.

Now let us look at the IP addresses belonging to sta1 and sta2.

```
mininet-wifi> sta1 ip addr show dev sta1-wlan0
187: sta1-wlan0: <BROADCAST,MULTICAST,UP,LOWER_UP> mtu 1500 qdisc mq state
↪  UP group default qlen 1000
    link/ether 02:00:00:00:00:00 brd ff:ff:ff:ff:ff:ff
    inet 192.168.0.1/24 scope global sta1-wlan0
        valid_lft forever preferred_lft forever
    inet6 fe80::ff:fe00:0/64 scope link
        valid_lft forever preferred_lft forever

mininet-wifi> sta2 ip addr show dev sta2-wlan0
188: sta2-wlan0: <BROADCAST,MULTICAST,UP,LOWER_UP> mtu 1500 qdisc mq state
↪  UP group default qlen 1000
    link/ether 02:00:00:00:01:00 brd ff:ff:ff:ff:ff:ff
    inet 192.168.1.1/24 scope global sta2-wlan0
        valid_lft forever preferred_lft forever
    inet6 fe80::ff:fe00:100/64 scope link
        valid_lft forever preferred_lft forever
```

Based on the above information, you can notice that sta1 is not on the same subnet as sta2. While sta1 is on subnet 192.168.0.0/24, sta2 is on subnet 192.168.1.0/24. However, since these two IP networks are directly connected to r1, the latter should know how to forward packets to them. So the different subnet addresses should not be a problem.

We still need to identify the cause of the problem. Let us check, then, sta1 and sta2's gateway. The *route -n* command can be used to check their gateway.

```
mininet-wifi> sta1 route -n
Kernel IP routing table
Destination Gateway  Genmask         Flags Metric Ref    Use Iface
192.168.0.0 0.0.0.0  255.255.255.0   U     0      0        0 sta1-wlan0

mininet-wifi> sta2 route -n
Kernel IP routing table
Destination Gateway  Conmask         Flags Metric Ref    Use Iface
192.168.1.0 0.0.0.0  255.255.255.0   U     0      0        0 sta2-wlan0
```

By checking the Gateway column in the results displayed above, you can see that no default gateway address is set for sta1 and sta2. Due to the absence of a default gateway, communication could not be established. You will then need to set the gateway address for the nodes. The commands demonstrated below define the gateway and allow you to verify whether they have been configured correctly.

```
mininet-wifi> sta1 route add default gw 192.168.0.100
mininet-wifi> sta2 route add default gw 192.168.1.100

mininet-wifi> sta1 route -n
Kernel IP routing table
Destination  Gateway        Genmask        Flags Metric Ref   Use Iface
0.0.0.0      192.168.0.100  0.0.0.0        UG    0      0       0 sta1-wlan0
192.168.0.0  0.0.0.0        255.255.255.0  U     0      0       0 sta1-wlan0

mininet-wifi> sta2 route -n
Kernel IP routing table
Destination  Gateway        Genmask        Flags Metric Ref   Use Iface
0.0.0.0      192.168.1.100  0.0.0.0        UG    0      0       0 sta2-wlan0
192.168.1.0  0.0.0.0        255.255.255.0  U     0      0       0 sta2-wlan0
```

Once the gateway address configuration is confirmed for both sta1 and sta2, let us try a new *ping* between them.

```
mininet-wifi> sta1 ping -c1 sta2
PING 192.168.1.1 (192.168.1.1) 56(84) bytes of data.
64 bytes from 192.168.1.1: icmp_seq=1 ttl=63 time=0.113 ms

--- 192.168.1.1 ping statistics ---
1 packets transmitted, 1 received, 0% packet loss, time 0ms
rtt min/avg/max/mdev = 0.113/0.113/0.113/0.000 ms
```

As you can see, sta1 and sta2 were able to communicate with each other.

This default gateway parameter is also used in any other network, including home networks, that has computers connected to the Internet. Without a default gateway, it would be relatively tricky to access the Internet.

Now let us run *<internet.py>*.

```
~/mininet-wifi$ sudo python mn-wifi-book-en/codes/cap4/internet.py
```

The above script includes a host named nat0, which will be the default gateway, as well as an access point and a station, as shown in Figure 4.5.

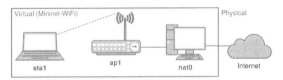

Figure 4.5: Internet topology.

So let us try to *ping* 8.8.8.8, a public address.

 The above IP address, 8.8.8.8, is a public DNS server address owned by Google and is often used worldwide to test Internet connectivity.

```
mininet-wifi> sta1 ping -c1 8.8.8.8
PING 8.8.8.8 (8.8.8.8) 56(84) bytes of data.
64 bytes from 8.8.8.8: icmp_seq=1 ttl=119 time=60.2 ms

--- 8.8.8.8 ping statistics ---
1 packets transmitted, 1 received, 0% packet loss, time 0ms
rtt min/avg/max/mdev = 60.284/60.284/60.284/0.000 ms
```

If all goes well, an output similar to the one shown above should be obtained, which results in a successful *ping* to 8.8.8.8. You can also use the *traceroute* command to trace the route of a given packet over the Internet, as follows.

```
mininet-wifi> sta1 traceroute google.com
traceroute to google.com (216.58.202.78), 30 hops max, 60 byte packets
 1  _gateway (10.0.0.2)  78.868 ms  77.030 ms  80.743 ms
```

```
 2  192.168.10.1 (192.168.10.1)   75.142 ms   84.139 ms   82.334 ms
 3  192.168.1.1 (192.168.1.1)   85.997 ms   87.625 ms   127.088 ms
 4  * * *
 5  100.122.80.79 (100.122.80.79)   136.739 ms 100.122.80.81 (100.122.80.81)
 ↳  142.876 ms 100.122.84.19 (100.122.84.19)   156.696 ms
 6  100.122.19.63 (100.122.19.63)   150.400 ms 100.122.25.82 (100.122.25.82)
 ↳  93.179 ms 100.122.25.80 (100.122.25.80)   86.603 ms
 7  100.122.25.171 (100.122.25.171)   90.418 ms   112.886 ms 100.122.25.167
 ↳  (100.122.25.167)   70.319 ms
 8  100.122.19.211 (100.122.19.211)   138.715 ms 100.122.20.81
 ↳  (100.122.20.81)   150.725 ms 100.122.20.91 (100.122.20.91)   153.799 ms
 9  72.14.220.142 (72.14.220.142)   147.798 ms 72.14.242.150 (72.14.242.150)
 ↳  157.341 ms   159.520 ms
10  108.170.245.225 (108.170.245.225)   115.825 ms 108.170.245.193
 ↳  (108.170.245.193)   121.135 ms 108.170.245.225 (108.170.245.225)
 ↳  124.587 ms
11  108.170.226.151 (108.170.226.151)   127.895 ms 108.170.226.227
 ↳  (108.170.226.227)   131.215 ms 108.170.226.151 (108.170.226.151)
 ↳  134.784 ms
12  google.com (216.58.202.78)   169.080 ms   106.478 ms   104.748 ms
```

 Why can sta1 communicate with the Internet? Because there was a default gateway address set for sta1. Without it, communication with the Internet would not be possible.

Note that there is indeed a default gateway address set for sta1.

```
mininet-wifi> sta1 route -n
Kernel IP routing table
Destination  Gateway    Genmask      lags Metric  Ref   Use Iface
0.0.0.0      10.0.0.2   0.0.0.0      UG   0        0     0 sta1-wlan0
10.0.0.0     0.0.0.0    255.0.0.0    U    0        0     0 sta1-wlan0
```

Whenever sta1 wants to communicate with any IP address (represented by IP 0.0.0.0) outside 10.0.0.0/8, it will forward packets to 10.0.0.2, so that 10.0.0.2 will forward packets to the intended address.

Conversely, if you remove the default gateway, you will be able to see how sta1 can no longer communicate with the Internet, as follows:

```
mininet-wifi> sta1 route del -net 0.0.0.0 gw 10.0.0.2
mininet-wifi> sta1 route -n
Kernel IP routing table
Destination Gateway  Genmask      Flags Metric Ref   Use Iface
```

```
10.0.0.0    0.0.0.0  255.0.0.0   U    0     0    0   sta1-wlan0

mininet-wifi> sta1 ping 8.8.8.8
connect: Network is unreachable
```

Physical nodes

 Requirement(s): WiFi network card

In addition to being able to establish communication between virtual nodes and the Internet, Mininet-WiFi also allows these virtual nodes to interact with any other physical node such as a laptop or smartphone, which are located near the computer that is running Mininet-WiFi.

In this new tutorial, we will create an access point using a USB WiFi network card, which should be connected to the computer running Mininet-WiFi. Therefore, in order to complete this tutorial, you will need to connect a USB WiFi network card to your computer, as illustrated in Figure 4.6.

Figure 4.6: WiFi network card connected to laptop.

After that, you need to edit *<hybridVirtualPhysical.py>* by modifying the value of the *usbDongleIface* variable. You can do so via the interface created by your operating system for the USB WiFi network card. The `ip link show` command can be used to find out the name assigned to the network card.

You will now need to identify the MAC address of the new interface. Since the interface name is *wlxf4f26d193319*, the following command allows you to visualize its address.

```
ip link show wlxf4f26d193319
437: wlxf4f26d193319: <NU-CARRIER,BROADCAST,MULTICAST,UP> mtu 1500 qdisc
↳  tbf state DOWN mode DEFAULT group default qlen 1000
link/ether f4:f2:6d:19:33:19 brd ff:ff:ff:ff:ff:ff
```

Then we add the MAC address to the *Network Manager* configuration file, located at *</etc/NetworkManager/NetworkManager.conf>*. Thus, the MAC address of the new WiFi card should appear on the list of devices not managed by *<NetworkManager.conf>*, as follows.

```
[keyfile]
unmanaged-devices=mac:f4:f2:6d:19:33:19;
```

 Network Manager is a utility program that aims to simplify the use of computer networks on Linux operating systems. When active, it will try to control the interfaces running on your computer. Once *Network Manager* gains control of the computer's network interfaces, the USB WiFi network card will not be able to operate in access point mode. Thus, we need to include it as a device that should be ignored by *Network Manager*.

Next, we need to restart the *Network Manager* process to apply the changes.

```
sudo service network-manager restart
```

Once the environment setup is complete, you need to run this tutorial's script.

```
~/mininet-wifi$ sudo python
↳  mn-wifi-book-en/codes/cap4/hybridVirtualPhysical.py
```

This script loads a virtual access point named ap1 and a physical access point that will make your physical network card operate in master mode. Mininet-WiFi will then bridge these two virtual and physical network interface cards (NICs), enabling virtual devices to communicate with physical ones and vice

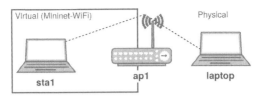

Figure 4.7: Interaction with physical nodes topology.

versa. Figure 4.7 illustrates the topology of this experiment.

Now connect another laptop or even your smartphone to the network you just created. Since the script does not include a DHCP server configuration, you need to assign your static IP address the following address: 192.168.0.0/24. It is the same subnet used by the sta1 station that was previously defined in the script. Taking into account that sta1 already has the IP 192.168.0.1, we will need to configure a different IP address. Let us consider 192.168.0.2/24 as an example.

Then use the Mininet-WiFi CLI to establish communication with your physical device.

```
mininet-wifi> sta1 ping -c5 192.168.0.2
PING 192.168.0.2 (192.168.0.2) 56(84) bytes of data.
64 bytes from 192.168.0.2: icmp_seq=1 ttl=64 time=2325 ms
64 bytes from 192.168.0.2: icmp_seq=2 ttl=64 time=1316 ms
64 bytes from 192.168.0.2: icmp_seq=3 ttl=64 time=294 ms
64 bytes from 192.168.0.2: icmp_seq=4 ttl=64 time=5.00 ms
64 bytes from 192.168.0.2: icmp_seq=5 ttl=64 time=115 ms
```

 If there is another network interface already using the 192.168.0.0/24 subnet, you will need to set up a different one.

Before we proceed to the next section, it is worth pointing out that the interaction between virtual and physical devices is not limited to making the USB WiFi card operate as an access point. Other modes of operation/commands such as *ad hoc*, *mesh* and *wifi-direct* can also be used.

• Ramon Fontes and Christian Esteve Rothenberg.*Mininet-WiFi: A Platform for Hybrid Physical-Virtual Software-Defined Wireless Networking Research*. In ACM SIGCOMM 2016 Poster & Demo Session, Aug 2016.

Rich Experimentation through Hybrid Physical-Virtual Software-Defined Wireless Networking Emulation: https://youtu.be/AbXLkUBLuDI

4.6.3   Decoding packets

Requirement(s): *Scapy*

Decoding packets is a process that allows us to parse the information contained in packets. We often only know this information conceptually, e.g. as the format of the IP header itself or even TCP, UDP, among many other parameters. Packet decoding will also be explored later (4.6.6) using Ryu, which will involve allowing the controller to parse the usernames contained in UDP packets.

In this tutorial, we will first explore packet decoding with an excellent packet manipulation tool, *Scapy*[9]. *Scapy* is a program written in Python that can forge or even decode packets from a wide variety of protocols, send them to the network, capture them, match requests and responses, among other actions.

Scapy can easily handle more classic tasks such as scanning, tracerouting, probing, unit testing, network attack or discovery, and can replace tools such as *hping*, *nmap*, *arpspoof* and *tcpdump*. It also works very well on other specific tasks that most other tools cannot handle, such as sending invalid frames, injecting customized IEEE 802.11 frames, and so on.

With this brief description of *Scapy* done, let us proceed to the next tutorial, whose purpose will be to decode ICMP packets that target a certain IP

---

[9]https://scapy.net/

address and create an action when the ICMP protocol and the specified IP are identified. As you may have guessed, we will use *Scapy*, which will require installing it. On its official website you can find instructions on how to do so.

Then, once *Scapy* is installed, you will need to create a file called *sta1.scapy* and add the code shown below to it.

```
from scapy.all import *

def pkt_callback(pkt):
    if IP in pkt:
        if pkt[IP].dst == '10.0.0.1':
            print("packet detected!")

if __name__ == '__main__':
    iface = sys.argv[1]
    sniff(iface=iface, prn=pkt_callback, filter="icmp", store=0)
```

This code will process ICMP packets that have 10.0.0.1 as their destination IP address. Should a match be found, the following message will be printed on the terminal: *packet detect!*.

Since we will need to run a topology to generate the necessary traffic, we will use the simplest Mininet-WiFi topology and start a terminal for sta1.

```
~/mininet-wifi$ sudo mn --wifi
mininet-wifi> xterm sta1
```

Using the sta1 terminal, you will run *sta1.scapy* by adding sta1's wireless interface as an argument, as follows.

```
sta1# python sta1.scapy sta1-wlan0
```

Then, using the Mininet-WiFi CLI, try a *ping* between sta1 and sta2.

```
mininet-wifi> sta2 ping -c5 10.0.0.1
PING 10.0.0.1 (10.0.0.1) 56(84) bytes of data.
64 bytes from 10.0.0.1: icmp_seq=1 ttl=64 time=0.132 ms
64 bytes from 10.0.0.1: icmp_seq=2 ttl=64 time=0.236 ms
64 bytes from 10.0.0.1: icmp_seq=3 ttl=64 time=0.155 ms
64 bytes from 10.0.0.1: icmp_seq=4 ttl=64 time=0.081 ms
64 bytes from 10.0.0.1: icmp_seq=5 ttl=64 time=0.126 ms

--- 10.0.0.1 ping statistics ---
5 packets transmitted, 5 received, 0% packet loss, time 4083ms
rtt min/avg/max/mdev = 0.081/0.146/0.236/0.051 ms
```

As a result, you should notice that the following output has been printed on the sta1 terminal.

```
packet detected!
packet detected!
packet detected!
packet detected!
packet detected!
```

Since five ICMP packets were sent by sta2, five messages are displayed on the sta1 terminal. Try modifying the *sta1.scapy* script file to change the displayed message or even the type of protocol to be processed.

Control over handover

 Requirement(s): *Scapy, Ryu*

In the field of wireless networks, one of the concepts that are most commonly asked about is handover, which is a process that is initiated when a mobile moves from its current cell to its neighboring cell, whether it be WiFi, LTE or any other type of wireless technology. There are two types of handover: horizontal handover, which involves cells of the same network technology, and vertical, which happens among different wireless network technologies.

In this tutorial, we will simulate a message received by a station as if it were sent by an SDN controller, instructing the station to associate with a certain access point. To do this, we will start *Ryu* on one terminal, and on the other one we will run *<handover-controller.py>*, which includes instructions on how to execute two scripts related to *Scapy* (*<sta1_.py>* and *<sta2_py>*) that will filter ICMP packets and, more importantly, echo request messages. Due to their importance, we recommend that you read and familiarize yourself with the contents of *<sta1_.py>* and *<sta2_py>*.

```
~/mininet-wifi/ryu$ sudo PYTHONPATH=. ./bin/ryu-manager
↪ ryu/app/simple_switch_13.py

~/mininet-wifi$ sudo python
↪ mn-wifi-book-en/codes/cap4/handover-controller.py
```

After starting the script, we will need to check the association between sta1 and sta2.

```
mininet-wifi> sta1 iw dev sta1-wlan0 link
Connected to 00:00:00:00:00:01 (on sta1-wlan0)
      SSID: handover
      freq: 2412
      RX: 25357 bytes (418 packets)
      TX: 1222 bytes (12 packets)
      signal: -52 dBm
      tx bitrate: 12.0 MBit/s

      bss flags:        short-slot-time
      dtim period:      2
      beacon int:       100

mininet-wifi> sta2 iw dev sta2-wlan0 link
Connected to 00:00:00:00:00:01 (on sta2-wlan0)
      SSID: handover
      freq: 2412
      RX: 84262 bytes (1483 packets)
      TX: 1554 bytes (16 packets)
      signal: -66 dBm
      tx bitrate: 24.0 MBit/s

      bss flags:        short-slot-time
      dtim period:      2
      beacon int:       100
```

Since the BSSID of ap1 is 00:00:00:00:01, we can confirm that both sta1
and sta2 are associated with it.

Now let us do something different: an attempt to *ping* h1 and sta1.

```
mininet-wifi> h1 ping -c1 sta1
```

Next, let us double check sta1's association status.

```
mininet-wifi> sta1 iw dev sta1-wlan0 link
Connected to 00:00:00:00:00:02 (on sta1-wlan0)
      SSID: handover
      freq: 2437
      RX: 9777 bytes (95 packets)
      TX: 644 bytes (6 packets)
      signal: -74 dBm
      tx bitrate: 1.0 MBit/s

      bss flags:        short-slot-time
      dtim period:      2
      beacon int:       100
```

As you can see, sta1 has migrated to the ap2 access point, whose BSSID is 00:00:00:00:00:02.

Now do the same with sta2.

```
mininet-wifi> h1 ping -c1 sta2
```

And also check sta2's association status.

```
mininet-wifi> sta2 iw dev sta2-wlan0 link
Connected to 00:00:00:00:00:03 (on sta2-wlan0)
        SSID: handover
        freq: 2412
        RX: 3952 bytes (68 packets)
        TX: 644 bytes (6 packets)
        signal: -88 dBm
        tx bitrate: 1.0 MBit/s

        bss flags:      short-slot-time
        dtim period:    2
        beacon int:     100
```

Likewise, sta2 has migrated to access point ap3, whose BSSID is 00:00:00:00:00:03.

Of course, the example used in this tutorial took into account the ICMP packet and in particular the *echo request* message. However, any other protocol could be filtered by *Scapy* in order to generate an action similar to the one generated by the *echo request* message.

Beacons

 Requirement(s): *Scapy, Ryu*

Scapy also allows beacon processing, which increases the range of available options for more accurate control over handover, mainly because beacons contain the signal strength that can be perceived by a node.

For example, consider the code shown below.

```
from scapy.all import *
import os
```

```
def pkt_callback(pkt):
    broadcast = "ff:ff:ff:ff:ff:ff"
    addr1 = "02:00:00:00:00:00"
    if pkt.haslayer(Dot11):
        extra = pkt.notdecoded
        signal = -(256 - ord(extra[-4:-3]))
        if pkt.addr1 == addr1:
            msg = "vehicle: %s / transmitter: %s / signal: %s" %
            ↪ (pkt.addr1, pkt.addr2, signal)
            packet = IP(src="10.0.0.2", dst="10.0.0.100")/TCP(sport=8000,
            ↪ dport=6653)/msg
            send(packet, verbose=0)

sniff(iface="mon0", prn=pkt_callback)
```

We can notice that the code includes an instruction to use the mon0 monitor interface. As we have seen in previous tutorials, monitor interfaces are capable of capturing *beacons* from the wireless medium. During the beacon capture process, (*pkt_callback*) is initiated if a beacon's target is the node through which the code is issuing a message. This message must be sent to the controller to inform it as to which node sent it, in addition to the signal strength perceived by that same node. Did you understand? Let us practice to learn more about this process.

First, you will run *Ryu* on a terminal, and on another one you will execute the <*handover-controller-beacons.py*> script.

```
~/mininet-wifi/ryu$ sudo PYTHONPATH=. ./bin/ryu-manager
↪ ryu/app/simple_switch_13.py

~/mininet-wifi$ sudo python
↪ mn-wifi-book-en/codes/cap4/handover-controller-beacons.py
```

Then run *Wireshark* on a third terminal and start the capture process using the con-eth0 interface. On it, you can see numerous packets sent by sta1 and sta2, which contain the messages displayed in the *Scapy* script. Figure 4.8 illustrates these messages. You can notice that a message was sent to IP address 10.0.0.100, i.e. the IP address on which *Ryu* is running. At the bottom of the figure, you can see the its content, which includes MAC addresses and the received signal, exactly as was defined for the *msg* variable previously. We reproduce this content below.

```
msg = "node: %s / transmitter: %s / signal: %s" % (pkt.addr1, pkt.addr2,
↳  signal)
```

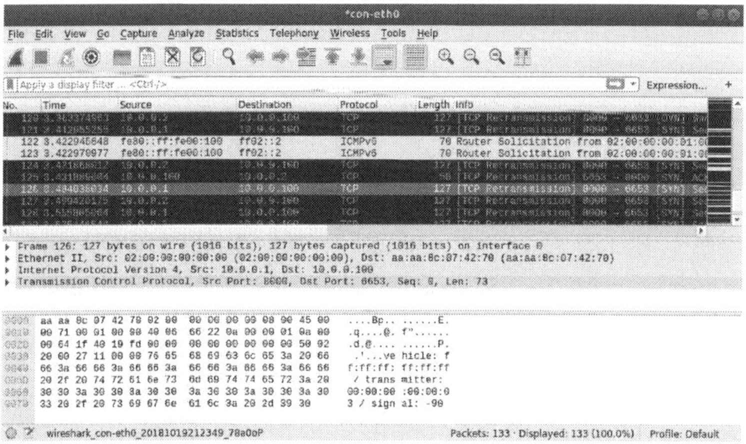

Figure 4.8: Packets sent by sta1 and sta2.

With this information the controller (or any application running on it, in fact), we will be able to take decisions and respond to the node, instructing it to transit to a new access point because of an observed low signal strength or even due to an access point overhead.

A good option for instructing stations to transit between access points based on instructions received by controllers is wpa_cli, which has already been used in the previous tutorial. To run wpa_cli, something similar to the code snippet below can be used.

```
os.system("~/mininet-wifi/util/m sta1 wpa_cli -i sta1-wlan0 roam
↳  00:00:00:00:00:02")
```

Written in *Python*, this code contains a new information, which is the *<util/m>* directory. This directory can be recalled from any terminal and also outside the Mininet-WiFi CLI. Its function is to execute commands from any node running on the Mininet-WiFi topology.

The previous command, then, executes wpa_cli from sta1 on the sta1-wlan0

interface and causes this node to associate with another access point that has
"00:00:00:00:00:02" as its BSSID. This type of association method (with the
roam command) is faster than using the disconnect and connect commands.

 Another good alternative that allows you to create (and "forge")
packets is *libtins*[10]. It is a software certainly worth learning about:
give it a try.

4.6.4   Association control

Two methods of association control are natively supported by Mininet-WiFi:
LLF (*Least-Loaded-First*) and SSF (*Strongest-Signal-First*). The first method
performs a type of load balancing of the number of stations that should be
associated with multiple access points. The second method instructs stations
to always search for an access point that provides a better signal strength.

To demonstrate these association control methods, let us run the following
script.

```
~/mininet-wifi$ sudo python
  ↪ mn-wifi-book-en/codes/cap4/associationControl.py
```

Using the SSF method, all stations will be associated with the ap1 access point.
The output below shows that one of the stations, sta5, is indeed associated
with ap1. *The same can be done with the other stations.*

```
mininet-wifi> sta5 iw dev sta5-wlan0 link
Connected to 02:00:00:00:05:00 (on sta5-wlan0)
        SSID: ssid-ap1
        freq: 2412
        RX: 1408 bytes (20 packets)
    TX: 306 bytes (4 packets)
    signal: -36 dBm
    tx bitrate: 1.0 MBit/s

    bss flags:      short-slot-time
    dtim period:    2
    beacon int:     100
```

---

[10]http://libtins.github.io/

Now, we need to edit the script and change the association control method from SSF to LLF. Next, let us double-check which access point the sta5 station is associated to.

```
mininet-wifi> sta5 iw dev sta5-wlan0 link
Connected to 02:00:00:00:06:00 (on sta5-wlan0)
        SSID: ssid-ap2
        freq: 2437
        RX: 12514 bytes (191 packets)
        TX: 806 bytes (9 packets)
        signal: -36 dBm
        tx bitrate: 1.0 MBit/s

        bss flags:      short-slot-time
        dtim period:    2
        beacon int:     100
```

As expected, sta5 is now associated with access point ap2 - and the same occurred with sta4. But what can explain this change? After executing the script, only sta4 and sta5 were within the signal range of the two access points included in the topology. As the first three stations were already associated with access point ap1, the requisites for using the new method were fulfilled, and consequently the method performed a type of load balancing, causing the new associations to be transferred to access point ap2.

Therefore, access point ap1 now has three associations, whereas the access point ap2 has two stations associated with it.

4.6.5 Forwarding by SSID

 Requirement(s): script(s) only

It is common for some companies or even homes to have access points that propagate multiple SSIDs. An access point may have multiple SSIDs for a number of reasons, including: to provide different security mechanisms for different access levels and/or users; to segregate bandwidth for different types of services; or even to reduce costs in relation to the number of access points.

In this tutorial, we will continue to use the OpenFlow protocol. This time, however, we will use it to define different rules for different SSIDs, which will cause OpenFlow to act on the different ports created by the access point for the various SSIDs.

Before we start this tutorial's script, we will need to stop *Network Manager*. To do so, we can use the following command.

```
~/mininet-wifi$ sudo service network-manager stop
```

 Connection to the Internet will certainly be interrupted when *network-manager* is stopped. After completing this tutorial, you can be re-establish connection by starting *network-manager* again.

Since *Network Manager* is no longer running, execute the following script.

```
~/mininet-wifi$ sudo python mn-wifi-book-en/codes/cap4/forwardingBySSID.py
```

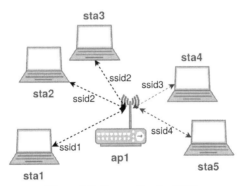

Figure 4.9: Forwarding by SSID.

This script will create five different SSIDs for access point ap1, as illustrated in Figure 4.9. At first, the script's rules say that sta1, sta2 and sta3 can communicate with each other. This can be confirmed after we perform the connectivity test among them.

```
mininet-wifi> sta1 ping -c1 sta2
PING 10.0.0.2 (10.0.0.2) 56(84) bytes of data.
64 bytes from 10.0.0.2: icmp_seq=1 ttl=64 time=1009 ms
```

```
--- 10.0.0.2 ping statistics ---
1 packets transmitted, 1 received, 0% packet loss, time 0ms
rtt min/avg/max/mdev = 1009.541/1009.541/1009.541/0.000 ms
mininet-wifi> sta1 ping -c1 sta3
PING 10.0.0.3 (10.0.0.3) 56(84) bytes of data.
64 bytes from 10.0.0.3: icmp_seq=1 ttl=64 time=0.516 ms

--- 10.0.0.3 ping statistics ---
1 packets transmitted, 1 received, 0% packet loss, time 0ms
rtt min/avg/max/mdev = 0.516/0.516/0.516/0.000 ms
mininet-wifi> sta2 ping -c1 sta3
PING 10.0.0.3 (10.0.0.3) 56(84) bytes of data.
64 bytes from 10.0.0.3: icmp_seq=1 ttl=64 time=0.336 ms

--- 10.0.0.3 ping statistics ---
1 packets transmitted, 1 received, 0% packet loss, time 0ms
rtt min/avg/max/mdev = 0.336/0.336/0.336/0.000 ms
```

As you can see, the rules defined in the script seem to work fine.

Yet the rules also say the following: sta4 and sta5 can communicate with each other, but since there are no rules that involve the combination of sta1, sta2 and sta3 with sta4 and sta5, these two groups of nodes will be separated, thus precluding communication between them.

For instance, note sta1's attempt to communicate with sta4 and sta5.

```
mininet-wifi> sta1 ping -c1 sta4
PING 10.0.0.4 (10.0.0.4) 56(84) bytes of data.
From 10.0.0.1 icmp_seq=1 Destination Host Unreachable

--- 10.0.0.4 ping statistics ---
1 packets transmitted, 0 received, +1 errors, 100% packet loss, time 0ms

mininet-wifi> sta1 ping -c1 sta5
PING 10.0.0.5 (10.0.0.5) 56(84) bytes of data.
From 10.0.0.1 icmp_seq=1 Destination Host Unreachable

--- 10.0.0.5 ping statistics ---
1 packets transmitted, 0 received, +1 errors, 100% packet loss, time 0ms
```

As expected, we receive *"Destination Host Unreachable"* as an answer and 100% of the packets were lost.

4.6.6   Security

In this section, we will complete security-related tutorials such as WPA/WPA2 key discovery, the "KRACK attack" case, intrusion detection system use, and centralized authentication using a RADIUS server.

ARP Spoofing

   Requirement(s): *dsniff*

The ARP (Address Resolution Protocol) is used to find the Ethernet address (MAC) that corresponds to a local IP address to which your computer wants to send a packet. Any host that is searching for a MAC sends out an ARP packet containing the IP address of the target host and waits for a response with the MAC address, which will be mapped to the host's IP address.

ARP Spoofing, in turn, is a type of attack that occurs when a "malicious element" receives this request and responds with its MAC address. It is a type of man-in-the-middle attack, during which the attacker can copy all traffic information to his machine before forwarding the data to the correct destination.

Part of this process is illustrated in Figure 4.10. You can infer that before reaching the final destination (the Internet), `sta2` is able to copy all traffic data, analyze them, and then forward them to the Internet without `sta1` having any knowledge about it.

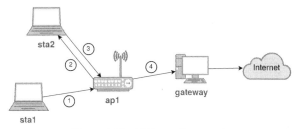

Figure 4.10: ARP spoofing attack.

In this tutorial, we will simulate the steps shown in the figure in order to demonstrate in practice how the ARP *Spoofing* attack occurs. To do so, let us run *<arpspoofing.py>*.

```
~/mininet-wifi$ sudo python mn-wifi-book-en/codes/cap4/arpspoofing.py
```

Then we will attempt to *ping* 8.8.8.8 from sta1.

```
mininet-wifi> sta1 ping -c1 8.8.8.8
PING 8.8.8.8 (8.8.8.8) 56(84) bytes of data.
64 bytes from 8.8.8.8: icmp_seq=1 ttl=118 time=68.8 ms

--- 8.8.8.8 ping statistics ---
1 packets transmitted, 1 received, 0% packet loss, time 0ms
rtt min/avg/max/mdev = 68.893/68.893/68.893/0.000 ms
```

As you can see, *ping* was successful. Now, let us check the sta1's ARP table. The table should include sta1's IP address as well as the MAC address of the default gateway.

```
mininet-wifi> sta1 arp -a
_gateway (10.0.0.3) at 0a:1e:54:0e:66:96 [ether] on sta1-wlan0
```

Now, let us simulate the ARP *Spoofing* attack and make sta1 mistake sta2 for its gateway without perceiving that the "gateway" is, in fact, sta2. First, open two terminals for sta2.

```
mininet-wifi> xterm sta2 sta2
```

Then, run *arpspoof* on the sta2 terminal, as follows. *If you do not have arpspoof, install it using the sudo apt install dsniff command.*

```
sta2# arpspoof -i sta2-wlan0 -t 10.0.0.1 10.0.0.3
```

The command described above induces 10.0.0.1, which is the victim, to think that 10.0.0.2 is now its default gateway. After issuing the command, we need to wait for a few seconds, then check sta1's ARP table again.

```
mininet-wifi> sta1 arp -a
_gateway (10.0.0.3) at 02:00:00:00:01:00 [ether] on sta1-wlan0
? (10.0.0.2) at 02:00:00:00:01:00 [ether] on sta1-wlan0
```

Here, we can notice that the MAC address of the default gateway is no longer the same as the one previously obtained.

Now, we will do a new *ping* from sta1 to 8.8.8.8 while using *tcpdump* on the sta2 terminal to confirm that sta2 is receiving traffic data sent by the victim.

```
sta2# tcpdump -i sta2-wlan0
20:30:34.970402 IP 10.0.0.1 > alpha-Inspiron: ICMP echo request, id 12251,
↪  seq 8, length 64
20:30:34.971552 IP alpha-Inspiron > 10.0.0.1: ICMP echo reply, id 12251,
↪  seq 8, length 64
20:30:35.430387 ARP, Reply _gateway is-at 02:00:00:00:01:00 (oui Unknown),
↪  length 28
20:30:35.972565 IP 10.0.0.1 > alpha-Inspiron: ICMP echo request, id 12251,
↪  seq 9, length 64
20:30:35.973722 IP alpha-Inspiron > 10.0.0.1: ICMP echo reply, id 12251,
↪  seq 9, length 64
20:30:36.973743 IP 10.0.0.1 > alpha-Inspiron: ICMP echo request, id 12251,
↪  seq 10, length 64
20:30:36.974884 IP alpha-Inspiron > 10.0.0.1: ICMP echo reply, id 12251,
↪  seq 10, length 64


mininet-wifi> sta1 ping -c10 8.8.8.8
```

After sta1 sends a few packets, you will be able to notice that sta2 received them, since sta1 was duped into perceiving sta2 as the correct default gateway.

Now sta2, the attacker, can use even simple tools like *sslstrip* to perform attacks via the HTTPS (*Hyper Text Transfer Protocol Secure*) protocol.

It is also worth mentioning that this type of attack can be avoided by using tools such as *ArpON* (ARP handler inspection).

Discovering WPA/WPA2 keys

 Requirement(s): *airodump-ng, aircrack-ng*

It is no surprise that WPA/WPA2 is a very secure protocol that is widely recommended and used in WiFi networks, especially when compared to WEP. However, it is possible for WPA/WPA2 keys to be discovered by means of brute-force attacks.

In this tutorial, we will learn how password discovery can be done. To do so, we will use a password dictionary as a basis to discover the password of a certain access point. We will also use two well-known tools to those who are familiar with wireless networks: *airodump-ng* and *aircrack-ng*.

Arodump-ng is used for capturing frames from 802.11 raw frames and is particularly suitable for collecting WEP, WPA and WPA2 IVs (Initialization Vectors) in order to use them with *aircrack-ng*. *Aircrack-ng*, in turn, is a network and packet sniffer that is widely used for WEP, WPA and WPA2 key wrapping.

To continue this tutorial, let us run <*authentication.py*>.

```
~/mininet-wifi$ sudo python mn-wifi-book-en/codes/cap4/authentication.py
```

And then, let us open a terminal for sta2.

```
mininet-wifi> xterm sta2
```

In the sta2 terminal, we will create a *monitor* interface, activate it and run *airodump-ng*, as follows.

```
sta2# iw dev sta2-wlan0 interface add mon0 type monitor
sta2# ip link set mon0 up
sta2# airodump-ng mon0
```

After a few seconds, you should be able to notice an output similar to the one shown below.

BSSID	PWR	Beacons	#Data, #/s	CH	MB	ENC	CIPHER	AUTH	ESSID
02:00:00:00:02:00	-35	20	0	0	1	54	WPA2	CCMP	PSK	ap1-ssid

BSSID	STATION	PWR	Rate	Lost	Frames	Probe
02:00:00:00:02:00	02:00:00:00:00:00	-35	0 - 1	0	1	ap1-ssid

This output should show all the access points that the client can "see". Based on this output, you need to save the *Basic Service Set Identifier* (BSSID) or MAC address of the access point - which in this case is ap1 - and add it to the following command.

```
sta2# airodump-ng --bssid 02:00:00:00:02:00 mon0 -w sniffer
```

This command, in addition to filtering captures using only the BSSID and chosen interfaces as selection criteria, saves all captures in a file called <*sniffer-01.cap*>, which can later be used for analysis.

Now, we will disconnect sta1 from access point ap1, since sta2 needs to capture authentication-related traffic information, which will include references to ap1's password. Although we will use the *disconnect* command, it is expected that sta1 will rejoin ap1, since there is a background process running wpa_supplicant that is responsible for negotiation/association between clients and access points.

```
mininet-wifi> sta1 iw dev sta1-wlan0 disconnect
```

Finally, let us create a file (e.g. *<password.psk>*) that contains a list of passwords, including the password of the ap1 access point. The correct password can be found in the script used in this tutorial. In a real situation, the password file should be replaced by a file that can be easily obtained on the Internet. Search for WPA/WPA2 Word List Dictionaries and you will certainly find a couple of references to the password dictionary.

Then we run *aircrack*, so that it can compare the contents of the password file named *<password.psk>* and the traffic data that sta2 captured when sta1 joined the ap1 access point.

```
sta2# aircrack-ng -w password.psk -b 02:00:00:00:02:00 sniffer-01.cap
```

And... *voilà*! *Aircrack* was able to discover the password of the ap1 access point, as can be seen below.

```
[00:00:00] 1/0 keys tested (234.69 k/s)

Time left: 0 seconds                                        inf%

                    KEY FOUND! [ 123456789a ]


Master Key     : AE 48 BB 45 8C C1 27 E0 B2 E0 06 8B 78 C6 3A 85
                 C1 F6 13 44 09 FC 89 9F 94 C5 AB 1F B2 C6 D9 E5

Transient Key  : 8F 77 37 71 F4 DE 6A F3 4A F2 B1 FC 81 85 C4 75
                 57 2A A4 87 DA FA 0E 8B 56 8A 19 D1 F6 84 6C 3F
                 08 F6 92 53 41 B1 CE 0D FB 81 50 CD 16 8D 20 B4
                 6D 2A AB 62 28 F7 2C 66 A5 47 89 DC 8E 1C 52 E2

EAPOL HMAC     : 53 2E 25 04 69 28 66 64 D1 8A AC 7C 82 6C FA 0
```

The 4-Way handshake

The key discovery described in the previous section was only possible because *airodump-ng* captured the WPA2 handshake. It is imperative to capture traffic data that include handshake messages, otherwise the password discovery process will not work.

 Handshake is the process by which a client and a server decide how to proceed with a connection, in which one recognizes the other and institutes that they are ready to initiate communication. To ensure the security of this conversation, a key must be installed and used only once.

Figure 4.11 depicts the four-way handshake of the WPA2 protocol that was captured in the previous tutorial, showing the same content as *sniffer-01.cap*. It is called four-way handshake because it involves the exchange of four messages between the access point and the client.

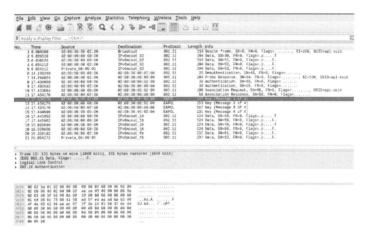

Figure 4.11: The four-way handshake.

The "KRACK attack"

 Requirement(s): *Ryu*

So far, we have used Ryu without making any changes to its source code. What if, then, we develop a program for Ryu and make it provide some kind of functionality for wireless networks? The tutorial we are going to do now concerns a case that was well-known among the wireless network community in 2017, when a researcher discovered a number of flaws in the WPA2 protocol.

The program we are going to create is based on the code developed by the author of the *"KRACK attack"*[11]. This code was adapted to run on Mininet-WiFi and also Ryu.

As we have already cloned the Ryu source code in 3.5.4, let us work with the script introduced in this tutorial, *<krack-attack.py>*. Please run it as follows.

```
~/mininet-wifi$ sudo python mn-wifi-book-en/codes/cap4/krack-attack.py
```

Then, check sta1's association status.

```
mininet-wifi> sta1 iw dev sta1-wlan0 link
Connected to 02:00:00:00:00:01 (on sta1-wlan0)
        SSID: handover
        freq: 2412
        RX: 11172 bytes (179 packets)
        TX: 1407 bytes (12 packets)
        signal: -68 dBm
        tx bitrate: 5.5 MBit/s

        bss flags:      short-slot-time
        dtim period:    2
        beacon int:     100
```

As you can see, sta1 is associated with access point ap1, which has an SSID called "handover".

Now let us go to the *Ryu* directory and load it along with the *krack_code.py* and *krack_app.py* modules, as follows:

---

[11] https://www.krackattacks.com/

```
~/mininet-wifi/ryu$ sudo PYTHONPATH=. ./bin/ryu-manager
↪ ryu/app/krack_code.py ryu/app/krack_app.py
```

Then change the position of sta1 so that it can associate with the ap2 access point. Then try to *ping* ap2, whose IP address is 10.0.0.102.

```
mininet-wifi> py sta1.setPosition('150,100,0')
mininet-wifi> sta1 ping 10.0.0.102
PING 10.0.0.102 (10.0.0.102) 56(84) bytes of data.
64 bytes from 10.0.0.102: icmp_seq=1 ttl=64 time=12.2 ms
^C
--- 10.0.0.102 ping statistics ---
7 packets transmitted, 1 received, 85% packet loss, time 6074ms
rtt min/avg/max/mdev = 12.285/12.285/12.285/0.000 ms
```

Then, check sta1's association status one more time.

```
mininet-wifi> sta1 iw dev sta1-wlan0 link
Not connected.
```

As we can see, sta1 is no longer associated with the ap2 access point.

What happened to sta1's association status? The program that we will load using *Ryu* has instructions enabling the controller to identify whether the access point - in this case, ap2 - has one of the four vulnerabilities exposed by the *"KRACK attack"*. Should it identify one of them, the controller will not allow sta1 to associate itself with the access point that is vulnerable, preventing sta1 from suffering attacks that exploit its identified vulnerability.

Now, let us return to the terminal on which *Ryu* is running.

```
[23:45:12] Detected FT reassociation frame
[23:45:13] Replaying Reassociation Request
[23:45:15] Replaying Reassociation Request
[23:45:16] Replaying Reassociation Request
[23:45:17] Replaying Reassociation Request
[23:45:18] Replaying Reassociation Request
[23:45:18] AP transmitted data using IV=1 (seq=15)
[23:45:18] AP transmitted data using IV=2 (seq=17)
[23:45:18] IV reuse detected (IV=-1, seq=17). AP is vulnerable!
Shutting Down AP2...
```

As you can see, a vulnerability has been detected on access point ap2. More-over, the controller has disabled it, undoing the association between sta1 and ap2 as a result.

Ryu's actions are not limited to just deactivating the access point ap2, of course. Other functions could be implemented, such as to notify stations without subsequent shutdowns or even to instruct access point ap2 to enforce security updates once vulnerabilities have been identified.

On the Krack Attack: Reproducing Vulnerability and a Software-Defined Mitigation Approach: https://youtu.be/XbUxH5zQPTc

Intrusion Detection System (IDS)

 Requirement(s): *Snort, hping3*

Intrusion Detection Systems (IDS) are systems that monitor traffic moving on networks and other systems to detect suspicious activities and known threats, sending alerts to the user when it finds such items. This way, it is possible to identify invasion attempts, allowing the control of authorizations and enabling the continuous improvement of network security.

In this tutorial, we will use *Snort*, a network intrusion detection program capable of doing real-time traffic analysis and packet registration on IP net-works. We will also use *hping3*, which is a free generator and parser of TCP/IP, a protocol used in security testing.

They can be installed via the apt command, as follows.

```
~/mininet-wifi$ sudo apt install snort hping3
```

Since this tutorial does not require the execution of a particular script, we will use the simplest Mininet topology, which consists of two hosts connected to a switch.

```
~/mininet-wifi$ sudo mn
```

Then we will open a terminal for h1, which will act as the IDS server.

```
mininet-wifi> xterm h1
```

On the h1 terminal, we will issue the following command, which will start *snort*.

```
h1# snort -d -l /var/log/snort/ -h 10.0.0.0/24 -A console -c
↪ /etc/snort/snort.conf
```

Then on h2, we will use *hping3* to generate data traffic to h1 in an attempt to simulate a denial of service (DoS) attack. While it is entirely possible to open a separate terminal for h2 and run the command below, execute it directly from the Mininet-WiFi CLI.

```
mininet-wifi> h2 hping3 -c 10000 -d 120 -S -w 64 -p 21 --flood
↪ --rand-source 10.0.0.1
HPING 10.0.0.1 (h2-eth0 10.0.0.1): S set, 40 headers + 120 data bytes
hping in flood mode, no replies will be shown
```

Now, again on h1, you can see packets being detected by *snort* as they are received by h1. An image similar to the one shown in Figure 4.12 should be observed.

Figure 4.12: Snort running on h1.

It is by using methods or programs similar to *snort* that professional *Pentesters* or security auditors identify vulnerabilities in the architecture of a company in order to exploit them. This identification and exploitation process can result in the delivery of reports that facilitate the correction of existing security breaches, as well as possible ones.

Centralized authentication

 Requirement(s): *FreeRADIUS*

Centralized authentication is an efficient and secure way to unify multiple authentication systems (e.g. address books, user data, Intranet, educational systems) on a single server. In this tutorial we will make stations associate in a centralized way, in which a server will be configured to respond to authentication requests.

To accomplish this, we will use the *RADIUS* authentication protocol. *RADIUS* (Remote Authentication Dial In User Service) is an authentication, authorization and accounting (AAA) protocol. It uses the UDP transport protocol (ports 1812 and 1813) for its communication process.

RADIUS' authentication function verifies user identity; its authorization function ensures that an authenticated user has access only to the authorized resources and, finally, the accounting function collects information about the resource utilization of a system caused by its users.

There are many different *RADIUS* servers, but in this tutorial we will use *FreeRADIUS*[12], one of the most popular *RADIUS* servers worldwide.

To get started, you will need to configure the *clients.conf* and *users* files, which should be located in the *FreeRADIUS* installation directory. In version 3.0.15, these files can be found at *</usr/local/etc/raddb/>*.

clients.conf and *users* should respectively have the following contents:

clients.conf

---

[12]`https://freeradius.org/`

```
client 127.0.0.1 {
        secret=secret
        shortname=sdn_ap
}
```

users

```
bob      Cleartext-Password := "hello"
joe      Cleartext-Password := "sdnteam"
```

Once *FreeRADIUS* is configured, let us start it in a terminal by issuing the following command.

```
~/mininet-wifi$ sudo radiusd -X
```

 The *FreeRADIUS* initialization and installation directory may vary depending on the installed version.

Now, while *FreeRADIUS* is running, you need to start *<radius.py>* on a new terminal.

 Note that in the *<radius.py>* script there is a configuration for stations that indicates the usernames and passwords to be used - i.e. users *bob* and *joe* and their respective passwords, exactly as defined in the *users* file.

```
~/mininet-wifi$ sudo python mn-wifi-book-en/codes/cap4/radius.py
```

Now you can notice some activity on the terminal from which *FreeRADIUS* was started. This activity concerns the communication between the *FreeRA-DIUS* server and the ap1 access point. If Wireshark is running, you can also see messages related to the *RADIUS* protocol exchanged among client, access point and *RADIUS* server, as shown in Figure 4.13.

Then, we can attempt to establish communication between sta1 and sta2.

```
mininet-wifi> sta1 ping -c1 sta2
PING 10.0.0.2 (10.0.0.2) 56(84) bytes of data.
64 bytes from 10.0.0.2: icmp_seq=1 ttl=64 time=1.13 ms

--- 10.0.0.2 ping statistics ---
1 packets transmitted, 1 received, 0% packet loss, time 0ms
rtt min/avg/max/mdev = 1.134/1.134/1.134/0.000 ms
```

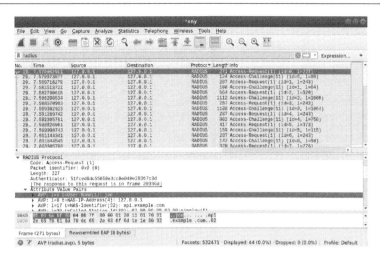

Figure 4.13: Capturing RADIUS protocol messages.

If the username and password did not match, it means that authentication could not be done successfully and `sta1` and `sta2` were unable to communicate with each other.

As an alternative to this tutorial, you could also start *FreeRADIUS* from any node, thus representing in a more reliable way what happens in the real world, where there would be a physical machine reserved for the *RADIUS* server.

Thus, since it is a relevant topic to this section of the book, in the following tutorial we will learn to start *FreeRADIUS* from a node, in addition to applying the SDN concept.

Mininet-WiFi working with FreeRADIUS:
`https://youtu.be/lpI9Mt5ggIs`

RADIUS and SDN

 Requirement(s): *Ryu, FreeRADIUS*

Applying the SDN concept to *RADIUS* can be very useful for many types of research. Different policies can be created and applied based on the username and not just on IP and MAC addresses, as usually happens. It would be possible, for instance, to restrict communication among clients that authenticate with the same username, apply QoS rules, among other possibilities.

Although we will not do any complicated tasks in this new tutorial, by completing it we can understand how the SDN controller can be used to perform traffic control based on usernames. To do so, we will again use Ryu, which will allow us to process packets and parse usernames. In *Ryu*'s source code, there is a module for the RADIUS protocol that was built based on its RFC 2865[13].

 Access the RADIUS RFC to understand how RADIUS support has been added to Ryu. For example, check, in section 3 (titled *Packet Format*), the available fields and their respective codes. Then compare the values defined in the packet format with the values in the *<radius.py>* file from the Ryu source code, at *ryu/lib/packet/*.

To start Ryu, let us use the following command.

```
~/mininet-wifi/ryu$ sudo PYTHONPATH=. ./bin/ryu-manager
↪  ryu/app/simple_switch_13.py
```

We will then run the tutorial script. It includes a node called h1 that will be the RADIUS server. The server is connected to switch s1, which in turn is connected to access point ap1.

```
~/mininet-wifi$ sudo python
↪  mn-wifi-book-en/codes/cap4/radiusCode-openflow.py
```

Stations sta1 and sta2 will attempt to authenticate to access point ap1 with the usernames *joe* and *bob*, respectively, as demonstrated in Figure 4.14.

---

[13]https://tools.ietf.org/html/rfc2865

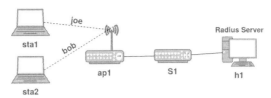

Figure 4.14: RADIUS topology.

When sta1 and sta2 try to authenticate to access point ap1, ap1 sends the authentication information to the RADIUS server via UDP port 1812. The RADIUS server is then expected to respond to the request by denying or accepting the authentication.

What happens is that the whole packet that has ap1 as the source and h1 as the destination must pass through the s1 switch. Thus, when s1 receives the request sent by ap1, in addition to forwarding the packet to h1, s1 also sends a copy of each UDP packet with destination port 1812 to the SDN controller (*see the script for more information*).

The modified version of *Ryu* is capable of sending packets on UDP port 1812 to a module or program, which can interpret the information and make a decision based on the received information. As a simpler example, the code will process usernames and MAC addresses of the node you wish to authenticate to ap1 and then print this information on the screen. *The output shown below was filtered in order to display only the information of interest to the tutorial.*

```
loading app ryu/app/simple_switch_13.py
loading app ryu.controller.ofp_handler
instantiating app ryu/app/simple_switch_13.py of SimpleSwitch13
instantiating app ryu.controller.ofp_handler of OFPHandler

Username: joe
Host: 02-00-00-00-00-00
Username: bob
Host: 02-00-00-00-01-00
```

As we can see, we were able to capture the usernames and MAC addresses of sta1 and sta2. However, we are not limited to this information, since all information in UDP packets can be parsed, including passwords. In order to parse more data, you will need to study RFC 2865 and edit *<radius.py>* according to the instructions contained in its RFC.

Studies that previously used Mininet-WiFi for research on security:
- Jacob H. Cox, Russell Clark, Henry Owen. *Leveraging SDN and WebRTC for Rogue Access Point Security*. IEEE Transactions on Network and Service Management, 2017.
- Abdul Jabbar Siddiqui and Azzedine Boukerche. *On the Impact of DDoS Attacks on Software-Defined Internet-of-Vehicles Control Plane*. International Wireless Communications & Mobile Computing Conference (IWCMC), 2018.
- Zhiheng Liu, Zhen Zhang, Yinzhi Cao, Zhaohan Xi, Shihao Jing, and Humberto La Roche Towards a *Secure Zero-rating Framework with Three Parties*. 27th USENIX Security Symposium, 2018
- Tahira Mahboob, Iqra Arshad, Aqsa Batool, Maryam Nawaz. *Authentication Mechanism to Secure Communication between Wireless SDN Planes*. 16th International Bhurban Conference on Applied Sciences and Technology (IBCAST), 2019.

Mininet-WiFi: RADIUS and SDN working together:
`https://youtu.be/2FjAS8g5Bsk`

4.6.7 6LoWPAN / IoT

Requirement(s): *Wireshark*

6LoWPAN (IPv6 over Low power Wireless Personal Area Networks) is an IP protocol that creates and maintains the specifications that allow us to use the IPv6 protocol on the IEEE 802.15.4 standard, which specifies the physical layer and performs access control for personal wireless networks with low transmission rates.

It has been widely used in the implementation of sensor networks with energy limitations, low signal range, low transmission rates and low cost. The integration of sensor networks with the Internet is seen as essential for the Internet of Things (IoT), allowing the use of distributed sensor applications.

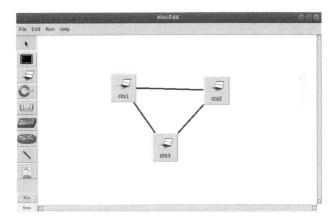

Figure 4.15: Nodes connected via 6LoWPAN.

6LoWPAN support on Mininet-WiFi is possible because of the *fakelb*[14] module, which is included in recent Linux kernel versions. Although there is still no adequate adaptation of the wireless medium for 6LoWPAN on Mininet-WiFi, its use is already possible and simple tests can be done.

To try out 6LoWPAN, we will use *MiniEdit* to generate the script for this tutorial. To do so, open the *MiniEdit*, add three stations, configure a *wpan* interface for each station and then create a link among them, setting them as a 6LoWPAN link (see the topology in Figure 4.15).

Once the topology is ready, export it as a script by naming the file as *<lowpan.py>*. Finally, with the script ready, *MiniEdit* is no longer needed and you can already run the newly created script.

```
~/mininet-wifi$ sudo python mn-wifi-book-en/codes/cap4/lowpan.py
```

Then, if everything occurred as expected while running the script, let us open

---

[14]https://github.com/torvalds/linux/blob/master/drivers/net/ieee802154/fakelb.c

Wireshark from sta1. Now, we can start capturing the sta1-wpan0 interface and test the *ping* between the nodes that integrate the topology, as follows.

```
mininet-wifi> sta1 ping -c1 2001::2
PING 2001::2(2001::2) 56 data bytes
64 bytes from 2001::2: icmp_seq=1 ttl=64 time=0.044 ms

--- 2001::2 ping statistics ---
1 packets transmitted, 1 received, 0% packet loss, time 0ms
rtt min/avg/max/mdev = 0.044/0.044/0.044/0.000 ms

mininet-wifi> sta1 ping -c1 2001::3
PING 2001::3(2001::3) 56 data bytes
64 bytes from 2001::3: icmp_seq=1 ttl=64 time=0.065 ms

--- 2001::3 ping statistics ---
1 packets transmitted, 1 received, 0% packet loss, time 0ms
rtt min/avg/max/mdev = 0.065/0.065/0.065/0.000 ms
```

 Note that we use the IPv6 address of the destination node as the IP, since 6LoWPAN uses the IPv6 protocol for addressing purposes.

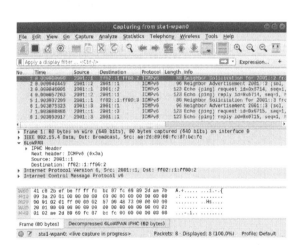

Figure 4.16: 6LoWPAN packets.

Finally, on *Wireshark*, we can note the presence of a few 6LoWPAN protocol-related packets, as shown in Figure 4.16. Two messages appear on Wireshark:

(a) *Neighbor Solicitation* and (b) *Neighbor Advertisement*. More information about these messages, as well as other explanations about the 6LoWPAN protocol, can be found in RFC 6775[15].

 The *fakelb* module is being replaced by mac802154_hwsim on recent Linux kernel versions.

Internet of Things

 Requirement(s): *mosquitto, mosquitto-clients*

The Message Queuing Telemetry Transport (MQTT) protocol is one of the main protocols aimed at using IoT functionalities. Extremely simple and lightweight, it is designed for low bandwidth consumption and hardware requirements, and its main use is to make the machines in a system talk in a process known as Machine-to-Machine (M2M). MQTT uses the publish/subscribe (pub/sub) paradigm to exchange messages. This paradigm implements a middleware called broker, which is responsible for receiving, queuing and firing messages received by publishers. The publisher is responsible for connecting to the broker and posting messages, and the subscriber, in turn, is responsible for connecting to the broker and receiving messages of interest.

Mosquitto, the prerequisite of this tutorial, will act as an intermediary between machines and protocols. Used with the MQTT protocol, Mosquitto makes the devices in a network talk to each other in an automated way. To complete this tutorial, consider having both *mosquitto* and *mosquitto-clients* on your computer. Information about Mosquitto's installation can be found at https://mosquitto.org/.

Now, let us start to the practice test. If *<lowpan.py>* is still running, keep it that way. Otherwise, start it again.

```
mininet-wifi> xterm sta1 sta2 sta3
```

---

[15]https://tools.ietf.org/html/rfc6775

From the `sta1` terminal, run *mosquitto*.

```
sta1# mosquitto
```

Now let us make it so that `sta2` is the subscriber of the topic called *test*.

```
sta2# mosquitto_sub -h 2001::1 -t "test"
```

Then, from `sta3`, we will send a message to this topic so that all nodes subscribing to it receive the message. As only `sta2` is a subscriber of the test topic, only it will receive the information sent by `sta3`.

```
sta3# mosquitto_pub -h 2001::1 -t "test" -m "message"
```

Now, note the message that has just been sent from the `sta2` terminal.

```
sta2# mosquitto_sub -h 2001::1 -t "test"
message
```

As previously stated, all subscribers of a given topic are be able to receive messages from nodes that publish information. Subscribers can also be publishers. This means that if `sta2` also sends a message, `sta3` would receive it.

Obviously, this was just a simple messaging test, but the MQTT protocol can be applied to projects in a variety of areas, such as industry, healthcare, transportation, and city and home planning.

Studies that previously used Mininet-WiFi for research on IoT:

- Deng, Guo-Cin; Wang, Kuochen. *An Application-aware QoS Routing Algorithm for SDN-based IoT Networking.* In: 2018 IEEE Symposium on Computers and Communications (ISCC). IEEE, 2018.
- Darabseh, Ala; Freris, Nikolaos. *A software-defined architecture for control of IoT cyberphysical systems.* Cluster Computing, 2019.
- Silvestre Apolonia, Nuno Miguel, et al. *Gossip-based service monitoring platform for wireless edge cloud computing.* Proceedings of the 2017 IEEE 14th International Conference on Networking, Sensing and Control (ICNSC 2017): May. 2017.
- Park, Seongjin, and Younghwan Yoo. *Network intelligence based on network state information for connected vehicles utilizing fog computing.* Mobile Information Systems, 2017.
- Coutinho, Antonio, et al. *Fogbed: A rapid-prototyping emulation environment for fog computing.* 2018 IEEE International Conference on Communications (ICC). IEEE, 2018.

Mininet-WiFi: first release towards 6LoWPAN:
`https://youtu.be/61YiKoOMyXM`

Mininet-WiFi working with Mosquitto (MQTT):
`https://youtu.be/LKTMiUyB6Lk`

4.6.8   Vehicular ad hoc networks

 Requirement(s): *Sumo, sumo-gui*

Vehicular ad hoc networks (VANETs) are a special class of mobile ad hoc networks (MANETs) consisted of vehicles equipped with wireless gadgets. VANETs have unique features that distinguish them from other mobile networks, such as the fast speed at which their nodes move and their highly modifiable topology, which make the links created between networked vehicles happen for only a few seconds and almost immediately.

How can the concept of software-defined wireless networks, or even software-defined vehicle networks, fit in the field of vehicular networks? Software-defined wireless networks can optimize network systems and are a suitable solution to deal with dynamic network environments, such as vehicular networks themselves. Furthermore, they increase the maximum number of connected devices and also provide software heterogeneity, among many other features.

And how can Mininet-WiFi be used as a support for research on vehicular networks? Mininet-WiFi is compatible with SUMO (Simulation of Urban MObility), one of the most used simulators in the world with regard to vehicular networks. In addition to its already well-known support of software-defined wireless networks, Mininet-WiFi has been used in several studies on vehicular networks. Let us see, then, how Mininet-WiFi can be used together with SUMO.

First, it is important that we have a map of the location that will be simulated. Mininet-WiFi comes with a pre-configured map that was extracted
from *OpenStreetMap*[16], a tool that is able to incorporate multi-way maps from
around the world, resembling Google Maps in this aspect.

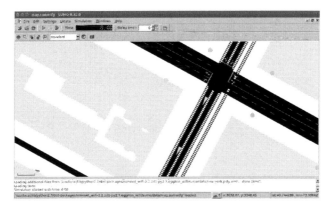

Figure 4.17: Simulation of Urban MObility (SUMO).

It will be quite simple to get our first vehicular network up and running on
Mininet-WiFi, since there is already a pre-configured script for such. Still,
you will need to install SUMO on your system first, in addition to *sumo-gui*
(Figure 4.17), a package that allows you to visualize the movement of SUMO's
simulated vehicles.

The SUMO version used in the writing of this tutorial was 1.1.0, but there
should be no complications if you decide to use a more recent version. In case
you notice any problems, feel free to contact the authors of this book.

Now, assuming SUMO is already installed, let us run *<vanet-sumo.py>*.

```
~/mininet-wifi$ sudo python mn-wifi-book-en/codes/cap4/vanet-sumo.py
```

Now, SUMO should be running and you have an opportunity to learn more
about *sumo-gui*, SUMO's graphical interface. Using *sumo-gui* you can start
the simulation, pause, filter objects like cars, among other actions. As the

---

[16]https://www.openstreetmap.org

simulated vehicles move, you can also use the Mininet-WiFi CLI to interact with them. The main integration between SUMO and Mininet-WiFi involves capturing vehicle positions. This means that if the Mininet-WiFi has the position data of the vehicles, the whole wireless part and network configuration in general is carried out by Mininet-WiFi.

Using the SUMO graphical interface, try to pause the simulation when the time reaches 20 seconds. Also try to visualize the vehicles numbered three and five. You will surely notice that they are located relatively close to each other. Therefore, it should be possible to test V2V or vehicle-to-vehicle communication, which is done among the vehicles without the need for eNodeB (*Evolved Node B*), the base station component of networks that use LTE (*Long-Term Evolution*), a mobile phone network standard. For Mininet-WiFi, eNodeB is nothing more than an access point.

So let us try to *ping* between the number three and five vehicles by issuing the command below. In SUMO, the number three vehicle is identified by car4 in Mininet-WiFi, since in SUMO's current configuration the node count starts at zero. The same goes for the vehicle number five.

```
mininet-wifi> car4 ping -c1 192.168.1.6
PING 192.168.1.6 (192.168.1.6) 56(84) bytes of data.
64 bytes from 192.168.1.6: icmp_seq=1 ttl=64 time=1.11 ms

--- 192.168.1.6 ping statistics ---
1 packets transmitted, 1 received, 0% packet loss, time 0ms
rtt min/avg/max/mdev = 1.116/1.116/1.116/0.000 ms
```

By default, all vehicles have two wireless interfaces: one working for V2I, which is an interface capable of associating with a base station; and another operating for V2V, working in mesh mode, which allows association to happen among vehicles. Both interfaces have the suffixes wlan and mp. They can be seen in the example below.

```
mininet-wifi> car4 ip addr show
1: lo: <LOOPBACK> mtu 65536 qdisc noop state DOWN group default qlen 1000
    link/loopback 00:00:00:00:00:00 brd 00:00:00:00:00:00
2: car4-mp1: <BROADCAST,MULTICAST,UP,LOWER_UP> mtu 1500 qdisc mq state UP
 ↪  group default qlen 1000
    link/ether 02:00:00:00:07:00 brd ff:ff:ff:ff:ff:ff
```

```
      inet 192.168.1.4/24 scope global car4-mp1
         valid_lft forever preferred_lft forever
  88: car4-wlan0: <BROADCAST,MULTICAST,UP,LOWER_UP> mtu 1500 qdisc mq state
  ↪  UP group default qlen 1000
      link/ether 02:00:00:00:06:00 brd ff:ff:ff:ff:ff:ff
      inet 192.168.0.4/24 scope global car4-wlan0
         valid_lft forever preferred_lft forever
      inet6 fe80::ff:fe00:600/64 scope link
         valid_lft forever preferred_lft forever
  89: car4-wlan1: <BROADCAST,MULTICAST> mtu 1500 qdisc mq state DOWN group
  ↪  default qlen 1000
      link/ether 02:00:00:00:07:00 brd ff:ff:ff:ff:ff:ff
```

 Although there is an interface named car3-wlan1, it is disabled. car3-wlan1 is used for creating the V2V interface, which works in mesh mode.

Finally, it can be seen, based on the commands shown below, that both interfaces (car3-wlan0 and car3-mp1) are associated with an access point and a mesh network, respectively.

```
mininet-wifi> car4 iw dev car4-wlan0 link
Connected to 00:00:00:11:00:04 (on car4-wlan0)
        SSID: vanet-ssid
        freq: 2412
        RX: 172521 bytes (3008 packets)
        TX: 7416 bytes (238 packets)
        signal: -63 dBm
        tx bitrate: 54.0 MBit/s

        bss flags:        short-slot-time
        dtim period:      2
        beacon int:       100

mininet-wifi> car4 iw dev car4-wlan0 info
Interface car4-wlan0
        ifindex 88
        wdev 0x3b00000001
        addr 02:00:00:00:06:00
        ssid vanet-ssid
        type managed
        wiphy 59
        channel 1 (2412 MHz), width: 20 MHz (no HT), center1: 2412 MHz
        txpower 14.00 dBm
```

Since SUMO does not include access point objects, especially base stations for wireless connections, it would be quite interesting if someone made an implementation in this regard, right?

All codes related to SUMO integration with Mininet-WiFi can be found in the *<mn_wifi/sumo>* directory. For instance, in this directory there is another folder called *data*, and inside *data* there is a file named *new-york.rou.xml*. By modifying the code in this file, you can define the number of simulated vehicles, at what point they begin to move in *sumo-gui*, in addition to all the edges the vehicles must travel.

 You may be wondering: how can I customize my own scenario and extract my map from *OpenStreetMap*? Once the SUMO part is ready[17], just replace the Mininet-WiFi files contained in the sumo/data directory and recompile the Mininet-WiFi code using `sudo make install`.

If you have successfully completed this tutorial and also understood how SUMO works, you can proceed to the following steps, which will involve applying the solutions presented throughout this chapter to vehicular networks. More information about SUMO can be found on its official website[18].

 Some studies to which SUMO can be (or was) applied:
- Campolo, C., Fontes, R., Iera, A., Rothenberg, C., Molinaro, A. Towards 5G Network Slicing for the V2X Ecosystem. Workshop on Advances in Slicing for Softwarized Infrastructures. NETSOFT. Montreal, Canada, 2018
- Al-Badarneh, J. Jararweh, Y. Al-Ayyoub, M. Fontes, R., Al-Smadi, M., Rothenberg, C. Cooperative Mobile Edge Computing System for VANET-Based Software Defined Content Delivery. Elsevier Computers and Electrical Engineering, 2018
- Badarneh, J. Jararweh, Y., Al-Ayyoub, M., Al-Smadi M., Fontes, R. Software Defined Storage for Cooperative Mobile Edge Computing System. SDS. Valencia, Spain, 2017

---

[17]http://sumo.dlr.de/wiki/Networks/Import/OpenStreetMap
[18]http://www.sumo.dlr.de/

Studies that previously used Mininet-WiFi for research on vehicular networks:

- Ramon dos Reis Fontes, Claudia Campolo, Christian Esteve Rothenberg, Antonella Molinaro. *From Theory to Experimental Evaluation: Resource Management in Software-Defined Vehicular Networks*. In IEEE Access, 2017.
- Seongjin Park and Younghwan Yoo. *Network Intelligence based on Network State Information for Connected Vehicles Utilizing Fog Computing*. Mobile Information Systems, vol. 2017.
- Zhenqian He, Bin Fu, Ao Cao, Jian Yu. *A Solution for Mobility Management in Software Defined VANET*. IEEE 15th International Conference on Mobile Ad Hoc and Sensor Systems (MASS), 2018.
- Kuldip Singh Atwal, Ajay Guleria, Mostafa Bassiouni. *SDN-based Mobility Management and QoS Support for Vehicular Ad-hoc Networks*. International Conference on Computing, Networking and Communications (ICNC), 2018.
- Soufian Toufga, Philippe Owezarski, Slim Abdellatif, Thierry Villemur. *An SDN hybrid architecture for vehicular networks: Application to Intelligent Transport System*. ERTS, 2018.
- C. Campolo, R. Fontes, A. Molinaro, Christian Esteve Rothenberg, A. Iera. *Slicing on the Road: Enabling the Automotive Vertical through 5G Network Softwarization*. Sensors, 18, 4435. 2018.

VANET-Based Software Defined Content Delivery Support for Cooperative Mobile Edge Computing Systems:
https://youtu.be/skyHDlHdwcs

Mininet-WiFi and SUMO: Tracking the position of the nodes:
https://www.youtube.com/watch?v=nywoltaRVSE

FAQ

Frequently Asked Questions

I have completed all tutorials. What would be the next step(s)?

The answer to this question depends on your goals. But in general, if the goal comes from the need to develop further scientific research and/or find out in which other fields of application Mininet-WiFi has been used, the citation catalogue is certainly a great reference point. It is continually updated and is available on the Mininet-WiFi source code page.

Nevertheless, we find it useful to provide you with a couple of lists of works that previously used Mininet-WiFi for research on topics such as video streaming, 5G, power management, and other technologies. They are displayed below.

Studies that previously used Mininet-WiFi for research on video streaming:

- Charles H.F. Santos, Felipe S. Dantas Silva and Augusto J. Venâncio Neto. *An Innovative Dynamic Bit Rate Streaming Approach to Improve Mobile User Multimedia Quality of Experience.* MobiWac, 2017
- Iulisloi Zacarias, Janaína Schwarzrock, Luciano Paschoal Gaspary, Kohl Anderson, Ricardo Q. A. Fernandes, Jorgito M. Stocchero, and Edison Pignaton de Freitas. *Enhancing Mobile Military Surveillance based on Video Streaming by Employing Software Defined Networks.* Wireless Communications and Mobile Computing, 2018.
- Daerawi, Kalamullah Ramli, Kalvein Rantelobo. *Performance Evaluation of Scalable High Efficiency Video Coding (SHVC) Transmission.* International Conference on Science and Technology (ICST), 2018.
- Reviakin, Aleksandr; Zahran, Ahmed H.; Sreenan, Cormac J. *dashc: a highly scalable client emulator for DASH video.* MMSys, 2018.
- Yueming Zheng, Ying Wang, Mingda Rui, Andrei Palade, Shane Sheehan and Eamonn O Nuallain. *Performance Evaluation of HTTP/2 over TLS+TCP and HTTP/2 over QUIC in a Mobile Network.* Journal of Information Sciences and Computing Technologies, 2018.

Studies that previously used Mininet-WiFi for research on 5G, power management, among other topics.

- Wang, Zeng, and Jinhe Zhou. *Power control mechanism in software defined wireless networking.* ICCSN. IEEE, 2016.
- Zhang, Xiao, Haijun Wang, and Haitao Zhao. *An SDN framework for UAV backbone network towards knowledge centric networking.* IEEE INFOCOM, 2018.
- Zacarias, Iulisloi, et al. *Combining software-defined and delay-tolerant approaches in last-mile tactical edge networking.* IEEE Communications Magazine, 2017.
- Mastorakis, Spyridon, Alexander Afanasyev, and Lixia Zhang. *On the evolution of ndnSIM: An open-source simulator for NDN experimentation.* ACM SIGCOMM Computer Communication Review, 2017.
- Canonico, Roberto, et al. *A framework to evaluate 5G networks for smart and fail-safe communications in ERTMS/ETCS.* International Conference on Reliability, Safety and Security of Railway Systems. Springer, 2017.
- Santos, I., et al. *Emulating a Software Defined LTE Radio Access Network Towards 5G.* International Conference on Communications (COMM). IEEE, 2018.

I do not have mac80211_hwsim installed on my computer. How can I get it?

Installing linux-image-extra will most likely install and compile mac80211_hwsim as well.

```
$ sudo apt-get install linux-image-extra-`uname -r`
```

I am trying to start Mininet-WiFi, but I am having errors. How can I solve them?

Most of the Mininet-WiFi runtime errors come from past executions that were not successfully completed. Therefore, it is often necessary to run the *sudo mn -c* command to clear any execution errors not properly completed.

How can I uninstall Mininet-WiFi?

To uninstall Mininet-WiFi, simply run the following command.

```
$ sudo rm -rf /usr/local/bin/mn /usr/local/bin/mnexec
  ↪ /usr/local/lib/python*/*/*mininet* /usr/local/bin/ovs-*
  ↪ /usr/local/sbin/ovs-*
```

I would like to know more about Mininet-WiFi. What do I need to do?

The Mininet-WiFi Handbook was created for both users and developers. This is undoubtedly the best document for information and troubleshooting about Mininet-WiFi. The mailing list (*mininet-wifi-discuss@googlegroups.com*) is also another important source to consult. It is frequently used by users who need new features or find Mininet-WiFi difficult in some situations.

- Web page:
  `http://mininet-wifi.github.io/`
- Mailing list *mininet-wifi-discuss*:
  `https://groups.google.com/forum/#!forum/`
  `mininet-wifi-discuss`

References

References

[Ago+16]   Elena Agostini et al. "OpenCAPWAP v2.0: the new open-source implementation of the CAPWAP protocol". In: *International Journal of Network Management* 26.6 (Sept. 2016), pages 537–552 (cited on page 12).

[Ber+14]   Carlos Bernardos et al. "An architecture for software defined wireless networking". In: *Wireless Communications, IEEE* 21.3 (June 2014), pages 52–61. ISSN: 1536-1284 (cited on page 11).

[Bin+12]   Md Asri Bin Ngadi et al. "A taxonomy of cross layer routing metrics for wireless mesh networks". In: *EURASIP Journal on Wireless Communications and Networking* 2012.1 (May 2012), page 177. ISSN: 1687-1499 (cited on page 7).

[Cal15]   Pat R. Calhoun. "Lightweight Access Point Protocol". In: Request for Comments 5412. RFC Editor, Nov. 2015 (cited on page 11).

[Cos+12]   Salvatore Costanzo et al. "Software Defined Wireless Networks: Unbridling SDNs". In: *Software Defined Networking (EWSDN), 2012 European Workshop on*. IEEE, Oct. 2012, pages 1–6. ISBN: 978-1-4673-4554-5 (cited on page 10).

[Del+12]   Peter Dely et al. "CloudMAC - An OpenFlow based architecture for 802.11 MAC layer processing in the cloud". In: *Globecom Workshops (GC Wkshps), 2012 IEEE*. IEEE, Dec. 2012, pages 186–191. ISBN: 978-1-4673-4942-0 (cited on page 12).

[Dor+15]   Avri Doria et al. "Forwarding and Control Element Separation (ForCES) Protocol Specification". In: Request for Comments 5810. RFC Editor, Oct. 2015 (cited on page 11).

[Enn+15]   Rob Enns et al. "Network Configuration Protocol (NETCONF)". In: Request for Comments 6241. RFC Editor, Oct. 2015 (cited on page 11).

[Fon+15]   R. R. Fontes et al. "Mininet-WiFi: Emulating software-defined wireless networks". In: *Network and Service Management (CNSM), 2015 11th International Conference on*. Nov. 2015, pages 384–389 (cited on pages 14–17).

[Han+15]   Bo Han et al. "Network function virtualization: Challenges and opportunities for innovations". In: *Communications Magazine, IEEE* 53.2 (Feb. 2015), pages 90–97 (cited on page 11).

[JK+14]   Nachikethas A. Jagadeesan, Bhaskar Krishnamachari, et al. "Software-Defined Networking Paradigms in Wireless Networks: A Survey". In: *ACM Comput. Surv.* 47.2 (Nov. 2014), 27:1–27:11. ISSN: 0360-0300 (cited on pages 10, 12).

[Kre+15]   D. Kreutz et al. "Software-Defined Networking: A Comprehensive Survey". In: *Proceedings of the IEEE* 103.1 (Jan. 2015), pages 14–76. ISSN: 0018-9219 (cited on pages 10, 88).

[Kum+13]   Swarun Kumar et al. "Bringing Cross-layer MIMO to Today's Wireless LANs". In: *Proceedings of the ACM SIGCOMM 2013 Conference on SIGCOMM*. SIGCOMM '13. Hong Kong, China: ACM, Oct. 2013, pages 387–398. ISBN: 978-1-4503-2056-6 (cited on page 12).

[LHM10]   Bob Lantz, Brandon Heller, and Nick McKeown. "A network in a laptop: rapid prototyping for software-defined networks". In: *Proceedings of the 9th ACM SIGCOMM Workshop on Hot Topics in Networks*. ACM. 2010, page 19 (cited on page).

[McK+08]   Nick McKeown et al. "OpenFlow: Enabling Innovation in Campus Networks". In: *SIGCOMM Comput. Commun. Rev.* 38.2 (Mar. 2008), pages 69–74. ISSN: 0146-4833 (cited on page 11).

[MSS14]   Sergey Monin, Alexander Shalimov, and Ruslan Smeliansky. "Chandelle: Smooth and Fast WiFi Roaming with SDN OpenFlow". In: 2014 (cited on page 12).

[Mou+15]   Henrique Moura et al. "Ethanol: Software defined networking for
            802.11 Wireless Networks". In: *IFIP/IEEE International Symposium
            on Integrated Network Management, IM 2015, Ottawa, ON, Canada,
            11-15 May, 2015*. IEEE, May 2015, pages 388–396 (cited on page 12).

[Rei+17]   Ramon dos Reis Fontes et al. "How Far Can We Go? Towards Realistic
            Software-Defined Wireless Networking Experiments". In: *Comput. J.*
            60.10 (2017), pages 1458–1471 (cited on pages 4, 11).

[Sam+15]   Malla Reddy Sama et al. "Software-defined control of the virtualized
            mobile packet core". In: *IEEE Communications Magazine* 53.2 (2015),
            pages 107–115 (cited on page 11).

[San+14]   M. A. Santos et al. "Software-defined networking based capacity shar-
            ing in hybrid networks". In: *2013 21st IEEE International Conference
            on Network Protocols (ICNP)*. Volume 00. Oct. 2014, pages 1–6 (cited
            on page 9).

[Sur+12]   Lalith Suresh et al. "Towards Programmable Enterprise WLANS with
            Odin". In: *Proceedings of the First Workshop on Hot Topics in Software
            Defined Networks*. HotSDN '12. Helsinki, Finland: ACM, Aug. 2012,
            pages 115–120. ISBN: 978-1-4503-1477-0 (cited on page 12).

[YGC15]   Lily Yang, Saravanan Govindan, and Hong Cheng. "Objectives for
            Control and Provisioning of Wireless Access Points (CAPWAP)". In:
            Request for Comments 4564. RFC Editor, Oct. 2015 (cited on page 11).

[Yap+10]   Kok-Kiong Yap et al. "Blueprint for Introducing Innovation into Wire-
            less Mobile Networks". In: *Proceedings of the Second ACM SIG-
            COMM Workshop on Virtualized Infrastructure Systems and Architec-
            tures*. VISA '10. New Delhi, India: ACM, Sept. 2010, pages 25–32.
            ISBN: 978-1-4503-0199-2 (cited on page 12).

Made in the USA
Columbia, SC
21 January 2023

10825941R00128